STRONGHOLD

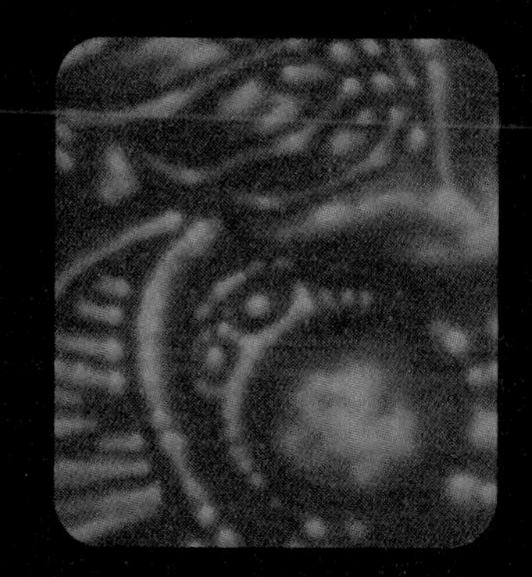

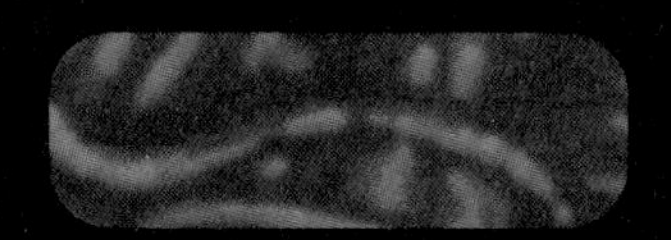

series editor
collection editor
collection designer
collection design manager

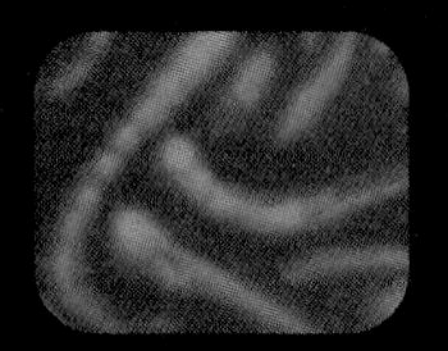

RYDER WINDHAM
LYNN ADAIR
TEENA GORES
BRIAN GOGOLIN

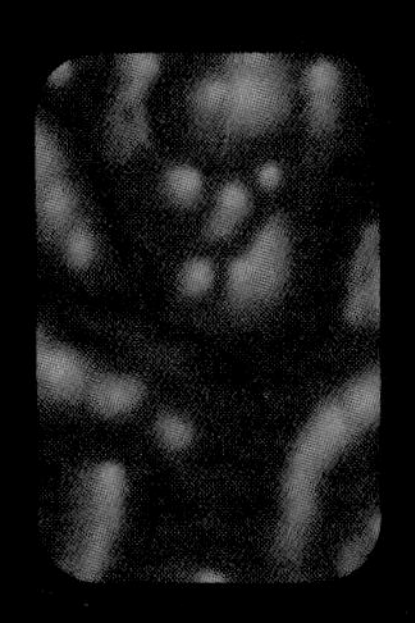

original Alien design by H. R. GIGER

special thanks to
Twentieth Century Fox
Film Corporation

ALIENS™

STRONGHOLD

script	JOHN ARCUDI
cover	DUNCAN FEGREDO
pencils	DOUG MAHNKE
inks	JIMMY PALMIOTTI
colors	PERRY McNAMEE
lettering	ELLIE de VILLE
introduction	MORT TODD

TITAN BOOKS

Published by
Titan Books Ltd.
42-44 Dolben Street
London SE1 0UP

October 1996
First edition
ISBN: 1-85286-733-7

1 3 5 7 9 10 8 6 4 2

Printed in Canada

ALIENS™: STRONGHOLD

This book collects issues one through four of the Dark Horse comic-book series *Aliens™: Stronghold.*

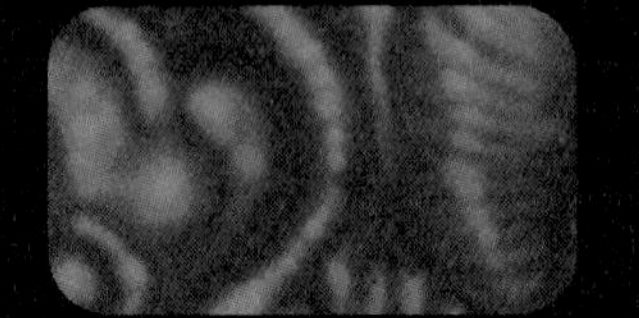

". . . IN COMICS, NO ONE CAN HEAR YOU SCREAM!"

Many people pick up the various Dark Horse *Aliens* products because of the original movie series, not because they are what you call traditional comics readers. And while comics and film are two similar but very different mediums of storytelling, this collection of *Aliens: Stronghold* is one of the most cinematographic comics ever published. This is due, in no small part, to the exceptional creative talents of writer John Arcudi and artist Doug Mahnke, who fashioned the four-issue series with such an amazing plot that you are forced to keep turning the pages as you absorb the visual detail and storyline. From the very first page, when Andy approaches the "camera" and it pulls out to reveal the Alien Queen, the pacing of the story and art draw you into *Stronghold* like a film would. Like a good horror movie, this story inspires fear, a sense of excitement, and plenty of laughs.

Laughs in an *Aliens* story? Sure! There's a thin line between horror and humor, and the Arcudi/Mahnke team knows how to straddle it like a bucking bronco. Amongst the gore, there are guffaws in a way that make the characters seem more real, if not more "human" (since many of the leads are not actually Homo sapiens). The tension between Dean and Jeri in *Stronghold* is amusing, and you wonder if the talking Alien synthetic has a high, nasally voice (that the French would love) when he banters with the armored, specialized synthetic, Dean. In some hands, it would be considered a creative crutch in the soundless medium of comics to further the plot by giving a usually speechless Alien a voice. Here, however, it adds to the singularity of Jeri. Besides, the creators have proven they can tell a story with a mute character, as seen in the recently released (and assuredly in the future, award-winning) Mask spin-off series, *Walter*.

There are several well-fleshed-out personalities in *Stronghold*, making you despise, relate to, or sympathize with the various characters. You become more involved as the story unfolds. Who is the actual villain of the story? Is it the Aliens? Caspar Nordling or the synthetic Dr. Payne? What is the true mission of Philip and Joy Strunk? Will Lizzy revolt? And can you really trust a talking, cigar-smoking Alien named

Jeff? These questions are raised and unexpectedly answered as the tale takes you on a roller-coaster ride of thrills, chills, and visceral spills.

Detail is paramount in an Arcudi script, and it really shines when combined with the art of Mahnke. Comics stories are not created in a vacuum (though *Stronghold* is set in one), and hard-core *Aliens* fans will notice elements from the movies and other Dark Horse *Aliens* series. Though working within existing continuity, Arcudi and Mahnke have succeeded in making this story their own.

Comics creators are not nurtured in a vacuum either. In case you didn't know, John and Doug have worked in comics for years, separately and together. They're most notably known as the original team that brought us that outrageous star of comics, film, and TV, The Mask, as we know him today. If you haven't read the first two *Mask* comics series, do yourself a favor and get the collected trade paperbacks of *The Mask* and *The Mask Returns* from Dark Horse and be ready to have some unadulterated fun. There you'll see the creative evolution of the Arcudi/Mahnke force that has flowered into *Walter* and the upcoming *Mask/Lobo* crossover from Dark Horse and DC Comics. On their own, Arcudi's and Mahnke's talents have complemented other popular titles, like John's run on *Barb Wire* (another comic/movie/comic) and Doug's contribution to the Dark Horse superhero, X. As with X, Doug's pencils for *Stronghold* are more than ably assisted by fan-favorite inker Jimmy Palmiotti, who plies his trade on the last three chapters.

Meanwhile (as they say in the funny books), sit back and get ready to witness an *Aliens* adventure bigger than the blockbuster movie series that inspired it, with enough plot twists and visuals to leave you twisted. You won't soon forget the horrific images and concepts within these pages. And remember . . . in comics, no one can hear you scream!

MORT TODD
NEW YORK, NY
1996

Mort Todd is a video director, producer, storyboard artist, and former editor in chief of Cracked *and the* Marvel Music *line of music comics. His eighth album cover for the* Back from the Grave *garage punk compilations has just been released from* Crypt Records.

OVER HERE!
I'VE LOCATED A FEW MORE.

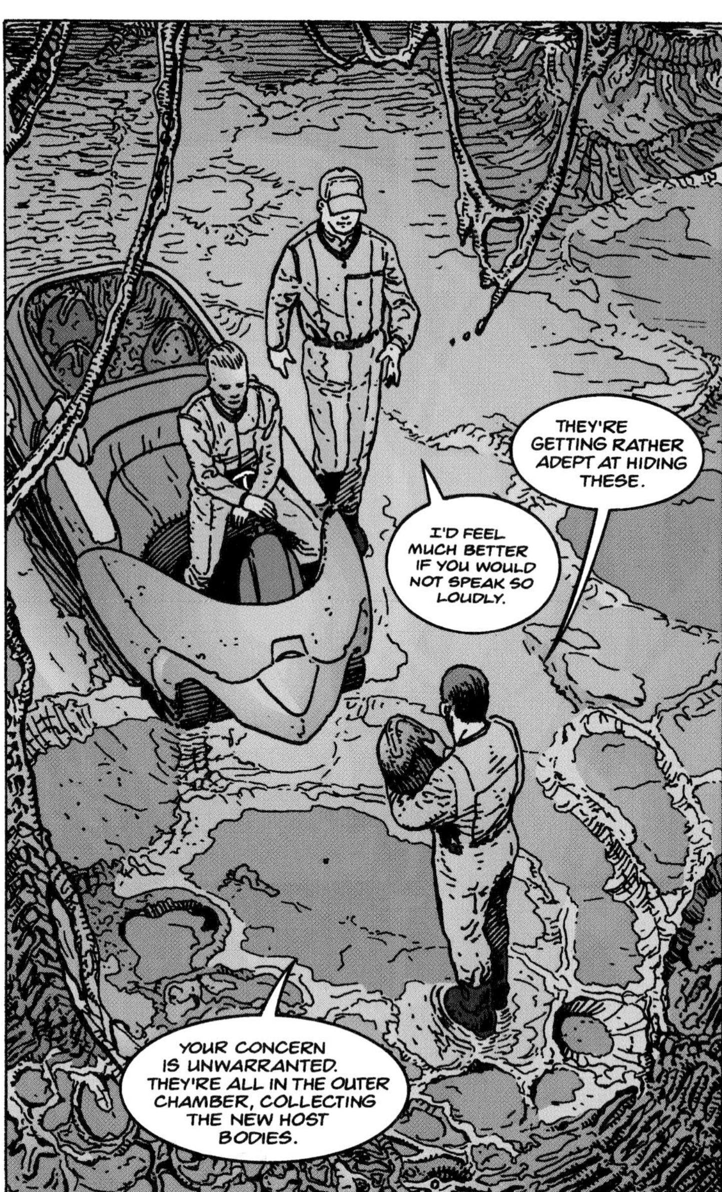
THEY'RE GETTING RATHER ADEPT AT HIDING THESE.
I'D FEEL MUCH BETTER IF YOU WOULD NOT SPEAK SO LOUDLY.
YOUR CONCERN IS UNWARRANTED. THEY'RE ALL IN THE OUTER CHAMBER, COLLECTING THE NEW HOST BODIES.

EVEN IF I WERE TO SHOUT, NONE OF THEM COULD HEAR ME ...
EXCEPT HER.

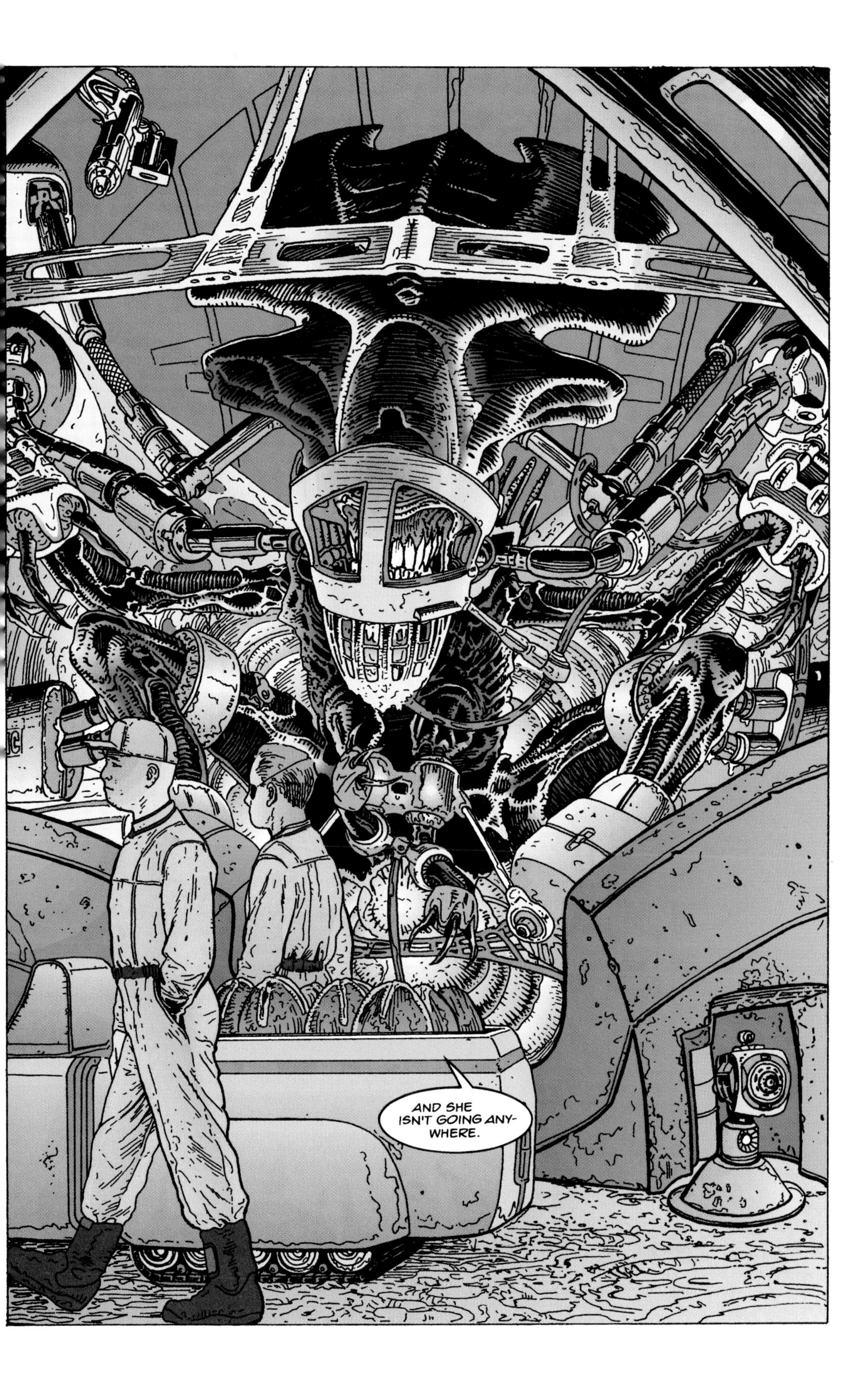
AND SHE ISN'T GOING ANYWHERE.

MAN, WILL I BE GLAD WHEN WE UNLOAD THESE.
BE-EP-EEP

PHIL! GET YOUR BUTT UP HERE!
WE'RE GETTING READY TO LAND.

WHERE WERE YOU?
DOWNSTAIRS, SECURING THE PARTS.

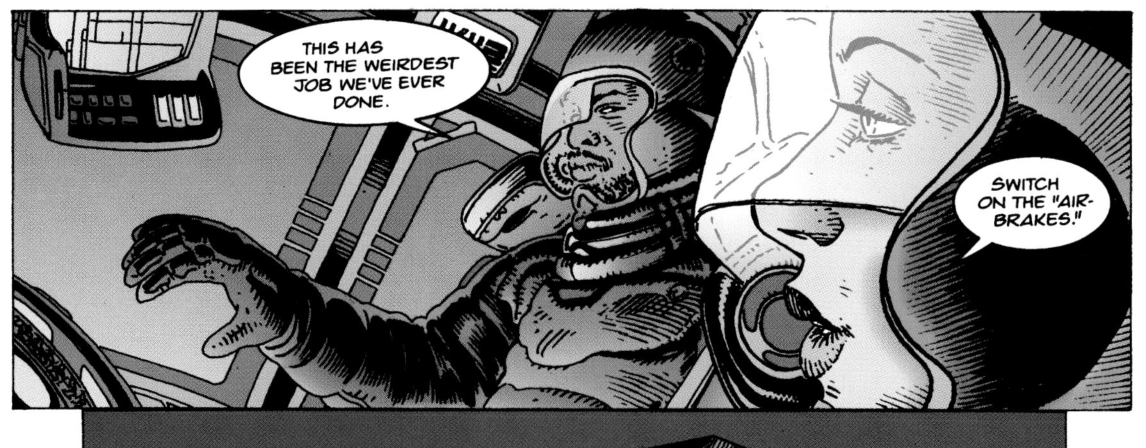
THIS HAS BEEN THE WEIRDEST JOB WE'VE EVER DONE.
SWITCH ON THE "AIR-BRAKES."

"YEAH, IT'S BEEN STRANGE ALL RIGHT...

"AND GETTING STRANGER."

THEY'VE JUST LANDED, DR. NORDLING—
I'VE CLEARED THEM FOR DOCK "C."
GOOD.
AT LAST, SOME DECENT COMPANY.
WHAT WAS THAT, SIR?
NOTHING.
TELL ANDY AND NED TO MEET ME DOWN AT THE DOCK.
YES SIR.

PRETTY BIG PLACE. HOPE THEY HAVE BATHTUBS HERE.
HEY, I'LL SETTLE FOR A HALFWAY DECENT SHOWER.
OH, I THINK WE CAN DO BETTER THAN THAT.
CASPAR NORDLING, AT YOUR SERVICE.
AND YOU MUST BE PHILIP STRUNK.
THAT'S RIGHT, AND THIS IS MY WIFE, JOY.
YOUR SPARE PARTS ARE IN THE CARGO BAY WITH YOUR OTHER SUPPLIES.
EVERY-THING IS CODED FOR RELEASE.
YOU BROUGHT PLENTY OF EYES, I HOPE?
ANDY HERE HAS HAD TO MAKE-DO WITH ONE FOR ALMOST TWO MONTHS NOW.

I'M SORRY ABOUT THE DELAY IN GETTING YOU YOUR PARTS, BUT—
AHH, FORGET IT. DEEP-SPACE TRAVEL IS EXPENSIVE.
GRANT-CORP CAN'T SCURRY OUT FOR EVERY REQUISITION. I KNOW THAT.

BESIDES, IT ISN'T LIKE THESE TWITS ARE ACTUALLY SUFFERING.
ANDY, YOU AND NED UN-LOAD THE CARGO.

C'MON, I'LL TAKE YOU TO YOUR QUARTERS. AFTER YOU WASH UP, I'LL INTRODUCE YOU TO JERI.
HE'LL BE HELPING YOU WITH THE HIVE SECURITY CHECK.
EXCUSE ME, DOCTOR, BUT SHOULDN'T WE BE HELPING THE SYNTHETICS?
NOT WITH *MY* BACK.
BUT IF *YOU* WANT TO, GO RIG AHEAD.
SO, YOU TWO ARE MARRIED.
MEET ON THE JOB?
OH, NO. WE WERE HIRED AS A MAINTENANCE TEAM *BECAUSE* WE WERE MARRIED.

THE LONG-TERM CLOSE QUARTERS CO-HABITATION THAT DEEP-SPACE TRAVEL REQUIRES CAN CAUSE FRICTION IN A CREW.
GRANT-CORP THOUGHT THAT MARRIED TECHNICAL TEAMS WERE AN IDEAL SOLUTION.
HOW PROGRESSIVE.
WHEN WAS YOUR LAST SECURITY SYSTEMS CHECK?
I DON'T KNOW, CAN'T REMEMBER THAT FAR BACK. FRANKLY, I DON'T SEE MUCH POINT IN IT.
OH, I KNOW IT'S YOUR JOB, BUT THIS SYSTEM IS FOOL-PROOF.
YOU'LL SEE WHAT I MEAN. THERE IS NO WAY ONE OF THOSE CREATURES COULD GET INTO THIS FACILITY.
AAAAAAAA

WHAT? WHAT IS IT?
BE-BEHIND YOU...

OH, THIS GUY?
THIS IS JERI.
MY, THAT WAS SOME SCREAM. YOU GAVE ME QUITE A SHOCK.
JERI, THIS IS PHILIP AND JOY STRUNK.
HOW DO YOU DO?
WE GAVE YOU A SHOCK?!

OH, THAT'S RIGHT. HE'S ONE OF YOUR SPECIALIZED SYNTHETICS.
CORRECT. MODELED AFTER THE MAYAKOVSKY PROTOTYPE.

MAYAKOVSKY? THAT NAME SOUNDS FAMILIAR.
DR. NORDLING, I WOULD REALLY LIKE TO GET TO OUR QUARTERS, IF YOU DON'T MIND.

OF COURSE. I'M SORRY. JUST AT THE END OF THIS HALLWAY.
CALL ME WHEN YOU'VE FINISHED.

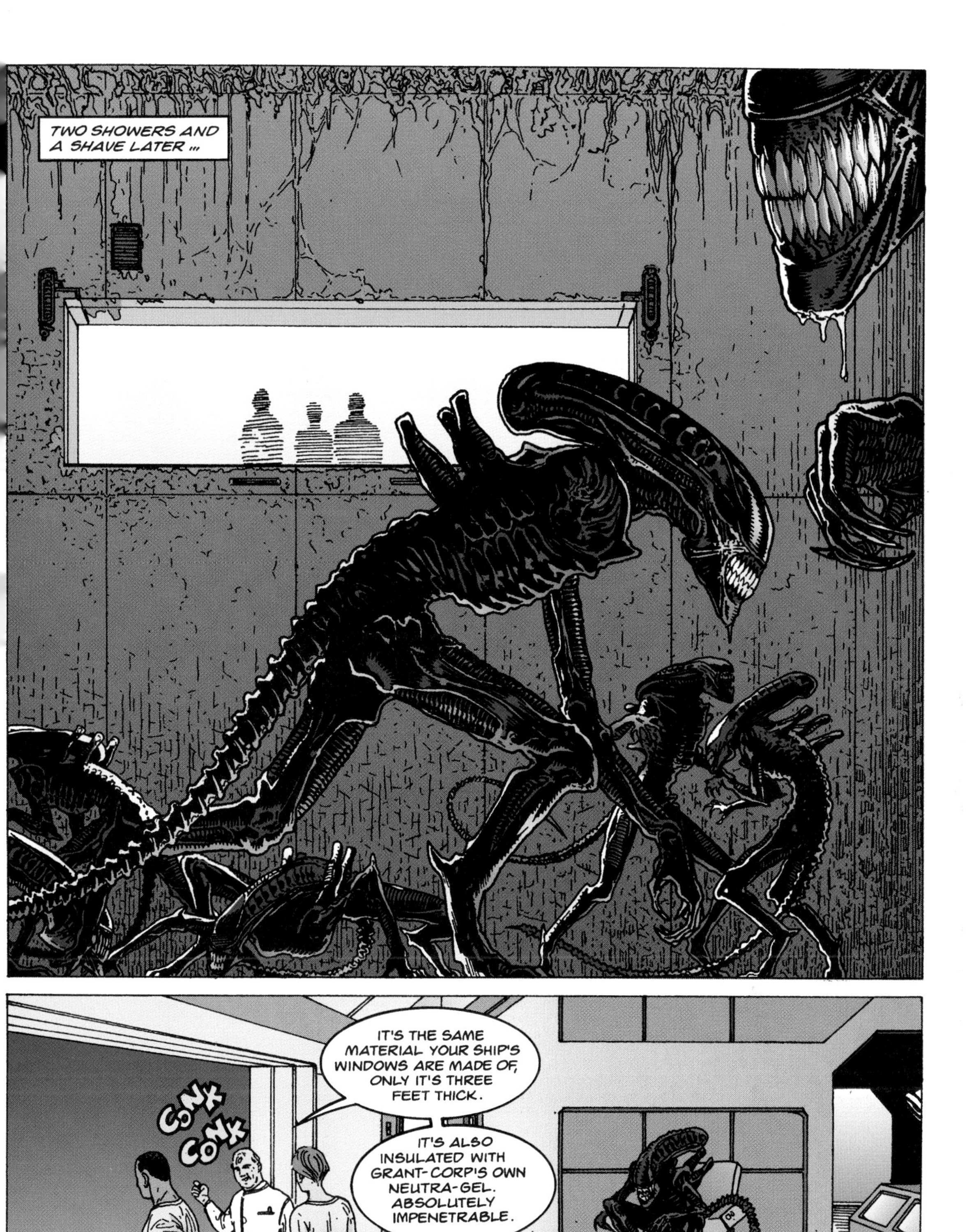

IT'S THE SAME MATERIAL YOUR SHIP'S WINDOWS ARE MADE OF, ONLY IT'S THREE FEET THICK.

CONK CONK

IT'S ALSO INSULATED WITH GRANT-CORP'S OWN NEUTRA-GEL. ABSOLUTELY IMPENETRABLE.

THAT ONE, WITH ONE ARM. IS THAT A CONGENITAL DEFECT, OR DID IT HAVE AN ACCIDENT?

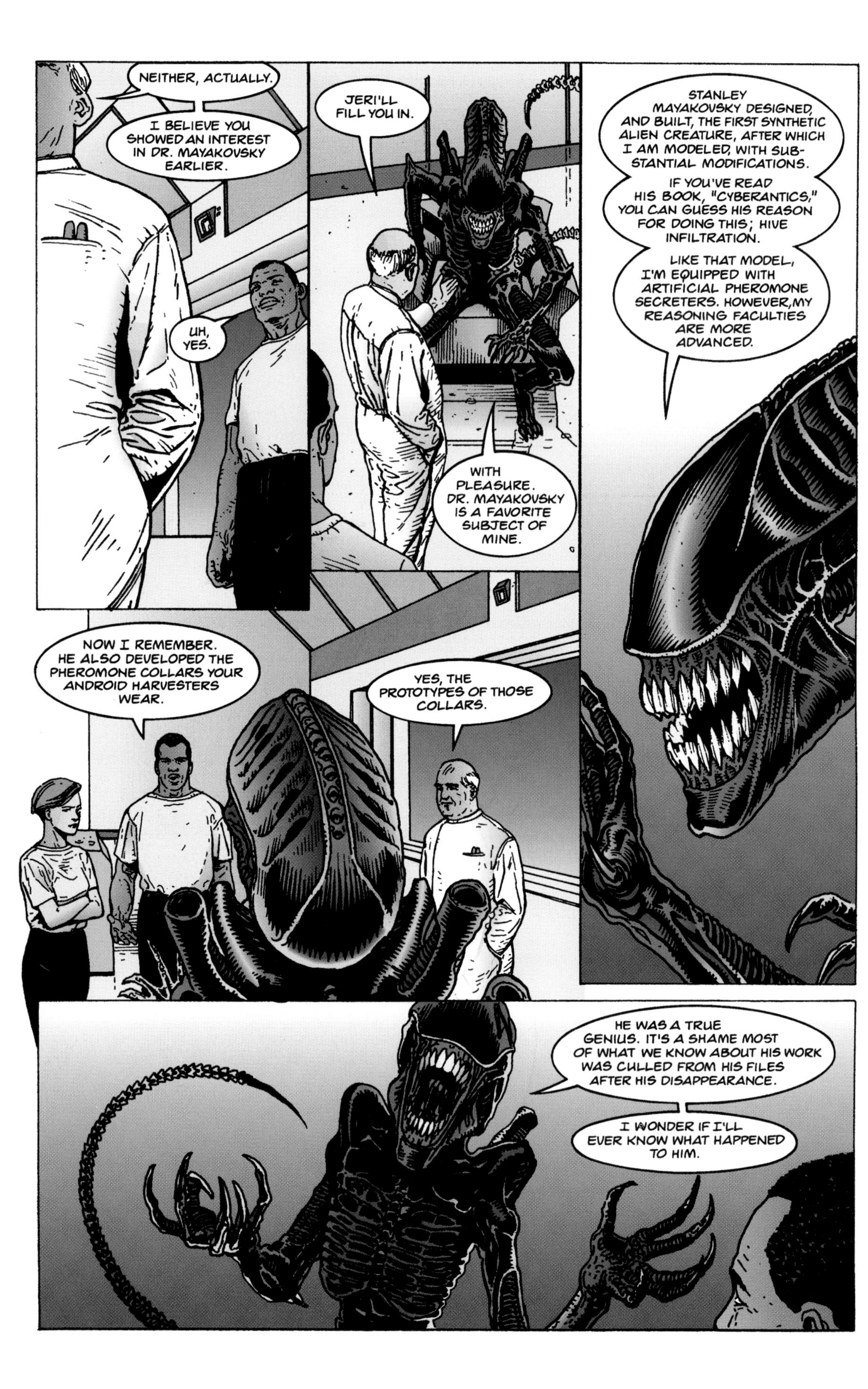

NEITHER, ACTUALLY.
I BELIEVE YOU SHOWED AN INTEREST IN DR. MAYAKOVSKY EARLIER.
UH, YES.
JERI'LL FILL YOU IN.
WITH PLEASURE. DR. MAYAKOVSKY IS A FAVORITE SUBJECT OF MINE.
STANLEY MAYAKOVSKY DESIGNED, AND BUILT, THE FIRST SYNTHETIC ALIEN CREATURE, AFTER WHICH I AM MODELED, WITH SUB-STANTIAL MODIFICATIONS.
IF YOU'VE READ HIS BOOK, "CYBERANTICS," YOU CAN GUESS HIS REASON FOR DOING THIS; HIVE INFILTRATION.
LIKE THAT MODEL, I'M EQUIPPED WITH ARTIFICIAL PHEROMONE SECRETERS. HOWEVER, MY REASONING FACULTIES ARE MORE ADVANCED.
NOW I REMEMBER. HE ALSO DEVELOPED THE PHEROMONE COLLARS YOUR ANDROID HARVESTERS WEAR.
YES, THE PROTOTYPES OF THOSE COLLARS.
HE WAS A TRUE GENIUS. IT'S A SHAME MOST OF WHAT WE KNOW ABOUT HIS WORK WAS CULLED FROM HIS FILES AFTER HIS DISAPPEARANCE.
I WONDER IF I'LL EVER KNOW WHAT HAPPENED TO HIM.

YOU KNOW, FOR AN ANDROID, YOU SURE GET MAUDLIN.
I KNOW WHAT'LL CHEER YOU UP.
YOU'RE GONNA LOVE THIS.
HAVE A CIGAR!
DR. NORDLING, DO I HAVE TO DO THIS?
SHUT UP AND START SMOKING.
NOW IS THAT A RIOT, OR WHAT?
IVA

ALL RIGHT, GIVE ME THAT! YOU'RE GETTING SLOBBER ALL OVER IT.
YOU TWO, FOLLOW ME.
WHERE ARE WE GOING?
THE LABORATORY. WHERE ELSE?
THIS IS WHERE I DO ALL MY WORK, AND YOU'LL HAVE TO BECOME FAMILIAR WITH IT FOR YOUR PURPOSES.
BUT FIRST, LET ME INTRODUCE YOU TO LIZZY, MY ASSISTANT.
A PLEASURE TO MEET YOU, MR. AND MRS. STRUNK.

NOW I DON'T KNOW HOW MUCH YOUR PEOPLE TOLD YOU ABOUT MY WORK, BECAUSE IT IS TOP-SECRET, SO LET ME GO OVER IT WITH YOU.
I'M WORKING TO DEVELOP A MICRO-ORGANISM THAT IS DEADLY TO THE CREATURES, BUT NOT PEOPLE. THE RAMIFICATIONS OF MY SUCCESS ARE ENORMOUS FOR GRANT-CORP.
I'VE HAD A LOT OF LUCK ENGINEERING SELECTIVE VIRUSES TO KILL PESTS, LIKE RATS OR WEEVILS, BUT THIS IS SOMETHING ALTOGETHER DIFFERENT.
HIGHLY SPECULATIVE. HIGHLY VOLATILE.
YOU'LL BE INSPECTING THIS MACHINE FOR ACCURACY. IT MONITORS ALL SEALS IN THIS LAB, ENSURING THAT IT'S AIRTIGHT.
WE WOULDN'T WANT ONE OF MY "UNPERFECTED" VIRUSES TO GET LOOSE.
NOT THAT IT WOULD HURT ANY OF MY *ALL-SYNTHETIC* STAFF. THEY ARE, OF COURSE, UNAFFECTED BY *ANY* VIRUS.
WELL, THANK YOU FOR EXPLAINING THAT, DOCTOR.
UMM, I'M CURIOUS, ISN'T IT LONELY HERE?

I MEAN, BEING THE ONLY HUMAN, AND ALL?
OH, SYNTHS AREN'T SUCH BAD COMPANY. IN FACT, THEY DON'T SMELL AS BAD AS SOME HUMANS I KNOW.
UNLESS THEY CUT THEMSELVES. THAT WHITE JUICE THAT LEAKS OUT REALLY *STINKS!*

AND THEY ALWAYS DO *EXACTLY* WHAT I TELL THEM TO.

BWAAAAA BWAAAAA BWAAAAA
AW, CRAP!
WHAT THE HELL IS THAT?!
THE HIVE ALARM. WE'D BETTER HEAD BACK TO THE OBSERVATION DECK.
"YOU SEE, SOMETIMES, THE HARVEST CREWS STAY IN THE HIVE TOO LONG.
"THE PHEROMONE COLLARS ARE ONLY GOOD IF YOU DON'T MOVE. THE CREATURES ARE VERY SENSITIVE TO MOTION.
"JUST BY YOUR MOVEMENT, THEY CAN TELL YOU'RE NOT ONE OF THEM.

"IT'S A NUISANCE, BUT NOT A REAL PROBLEM.
"DEAN WILL GET IN THERE AND CLEAN IT UP IN NO TIME."
"OH, RIGHT. DEAN IS YOUR OTHER SPECIALIZED SYNTHETIC."
"YEAH, AND WELL EQUIPPED FOR THE TASK.
"A THREE-TON TITANIUM EXOSKELETON, FULLY ARMORED, AND THAT'S COVERED WITH A NEUTRA-GEL LINED OUTER SKIN.
"HE ISN'T LACKING FOR FIRE-POWER EITHER.

"A PLASMA RIFLE OF OBSCENE CONCUSSIVE FORCE, WITH AN ALMOST INEXHAUSTIBLE ENERGY SUPPLY.

"THERMITE GRENADES, FLAME THROWERS, AND A FEW OTHER THINGS.

"IT'S BEEN A WHILE SINCE I READ THE MANUAL.

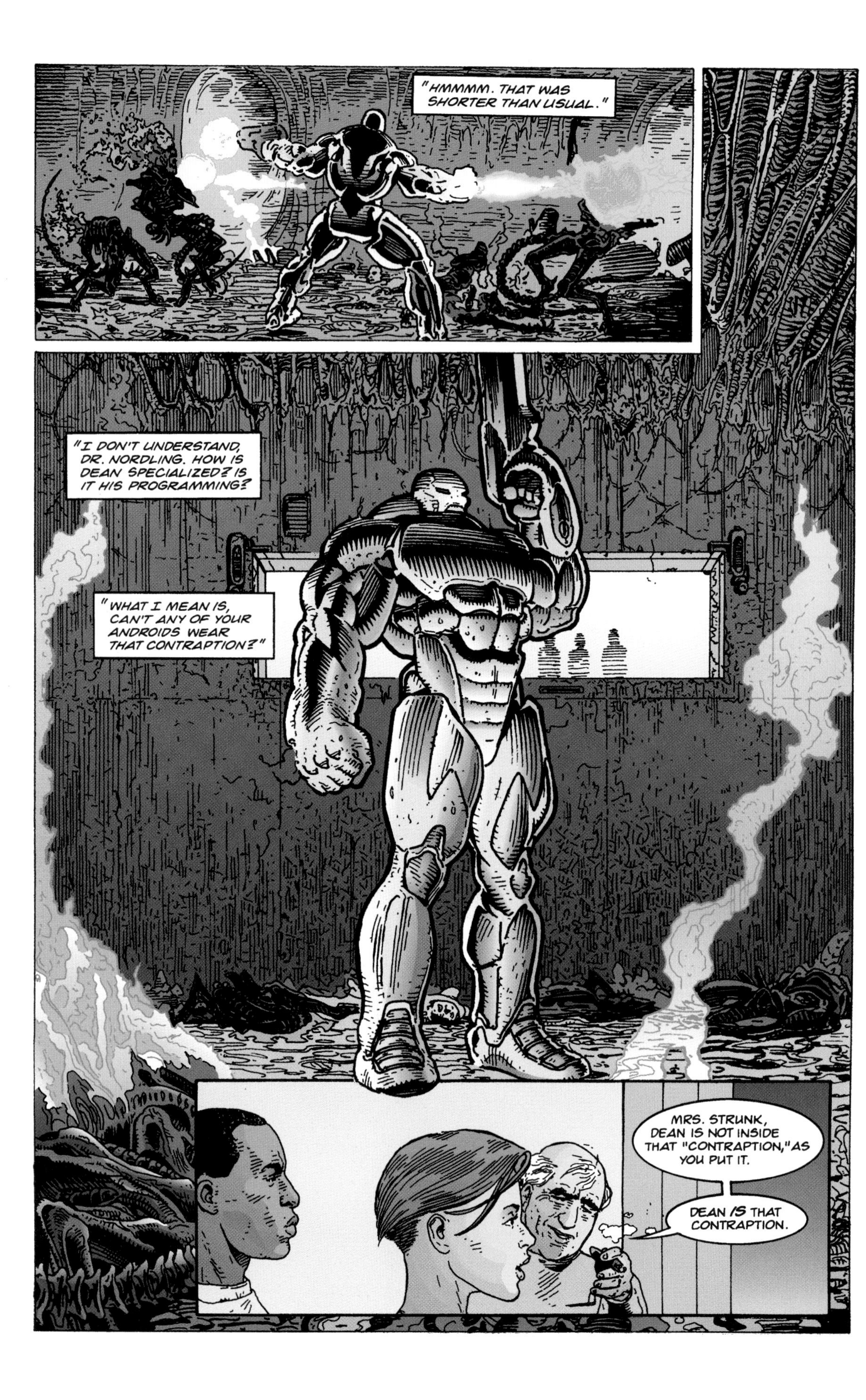
"HMMMM. THAT WAS SHORTER THAN USUAL."
"I DON'T UNDERSTAND, DR. NORDLING. HOW IS DEAN SPECIALIZED? IS IT HIS PROGRAMMING?
"WHAT I MEAN IS, CAN'T ANY OF YOUR ANDROIDS WEAR THAT CONTRAPTION?"
MRS. STRUNK, DEAN IS NOT INSIDE THAT "CONTRAPTION," AS YOU PUT IT.
DEAN IS THAT CONTRAPTION.

JERI, RETRIEVE THE EGG CART AND BODY PARTS.
OH, ALL RIGHT.
CORRECT ME IF I'M WRONG, BUT THAT ANDROID SOUNDED AWFULLY RELUCTANT TO GO IN THERE.
NO, YOU'RE QUITE RIGHT.
EVERYONE KNOWS THAT ANDROIDS ARE PROGRAMMED TO PROTECT HUMANS AT ALL COSTS, AND NEVER HARM THEM. A PRIME DIRECTIVE, IF YOU WILL.
BEEP BEEP
"WHAT'S NOT SO WELL KNOWN IS THEIR SECONDARY MANDATE OF SELF-PRESERVATION.
"WITHOUT IT, THEY COULDN'T FUNCTION PROPERLY."
"YOU'RE SAYING HE'S AFRAID OF THE CREATURES?"
"NO. JERI IS NOT AFRAID OF ANYTHING.

"IT'S JUST THAT JERI AND DEAN DON'T GET ALONG.
"DEAN REALLY ONLY HAS TWO FUNCTIONS: IDENTIFY AND DESTROY THE ALIEN CREATURES.

"JERI'S FUNCTION IS TO BE ONE OF THE CREATURES. HE LOOKS LIKE THEY DO, MOVES AND SMELLS LIKE THEY DO.
"IF HE WANTS TO, HE CAN EVEN SOUND LIKE THEY DO."
DEAN IT'S ME! IT'S JERI!

"THE ONLY WAY JERI CAN KEEP FROM BEING SHOT IS TO TALK. DEAN **KNOWS** THAT THE CREATURES CAN'T TALK."
"OF COURSE, I'M SUPPOSED TO ALERT DEAN THAT JERI IS ENTERING THE HIVE, AND NOT TO FIRE ON HIM..."
ALL RIGHT.

BUT IT'S A LOT MORE FUN THIS WAY.

DOCTOR NOR—
WELL, IT'S GETTING PRETTY LATE, AND I IMAGINE YOU MUST BE RATHER TIRED.

LET'S SEE IF WE CAN SCARE UP SOME EXTRA SHEETS FOR YOU.

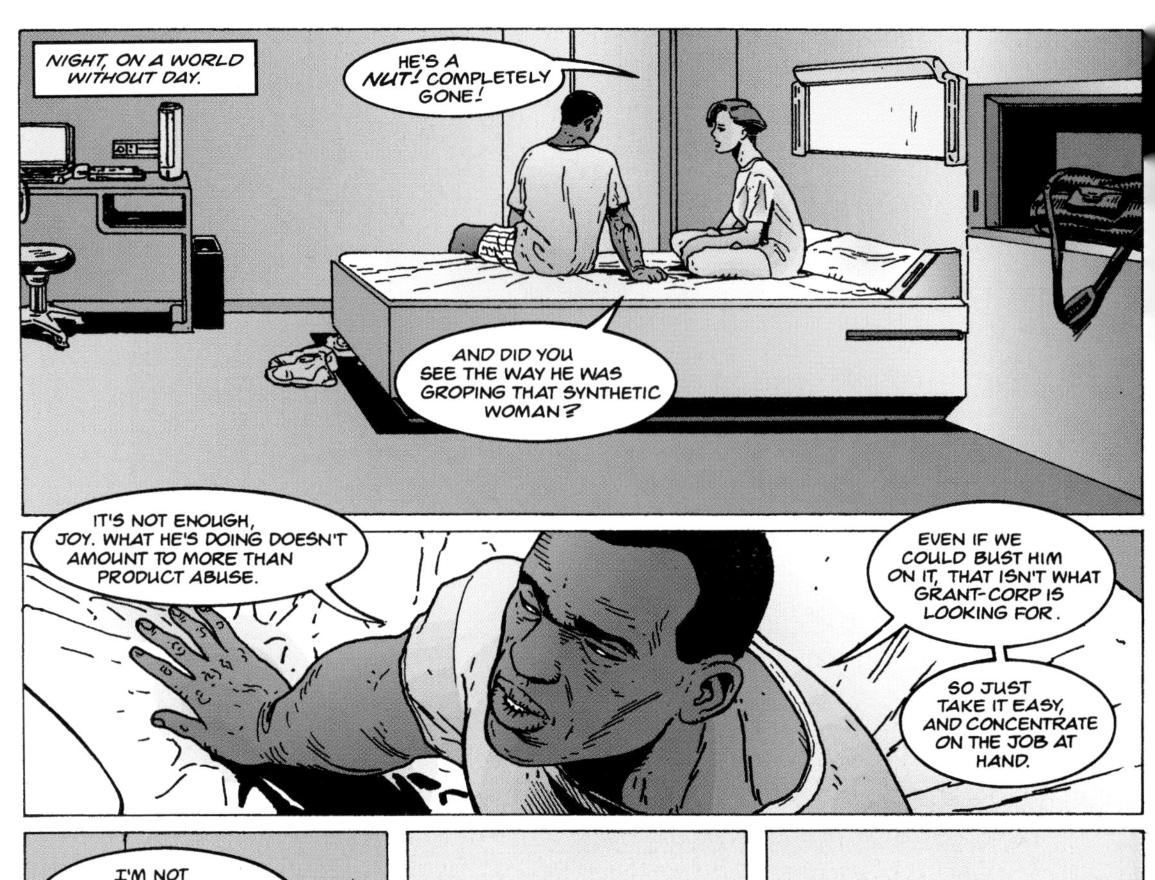
NIGHT, ON A WORLD WITHOUT DAY.
HE'S A NUT! COMPLETELY GONE!
AND DID YOU SEE THE WAY HE WAS GROPING THAT SYNTHETIC WOMAN?
IT'S NOT ENOUGH, JOY. WHAT HE'S DOING DOESN'T AMOUNT TO MORE THAN PRODUCT ABUSE.
EVEN IF WE COULD BUST HIM ON IT, THAT ISN'T WHAT GRANT-CORP IS LOOKING FOR.
SO JUST TAKE IT EASY, AND CONCENTRATE ON THE JOB AT HAND.

I'M NOT GOING TO TAKE IT EASY, BUT I'LL HANDLE MY END.
DON'T WORRY, HONEY. IF THE EXECS AT GRANT-CORP ARE RIGHT...
...NORDLING WILL BE PUT AWAY FOR LIFE.

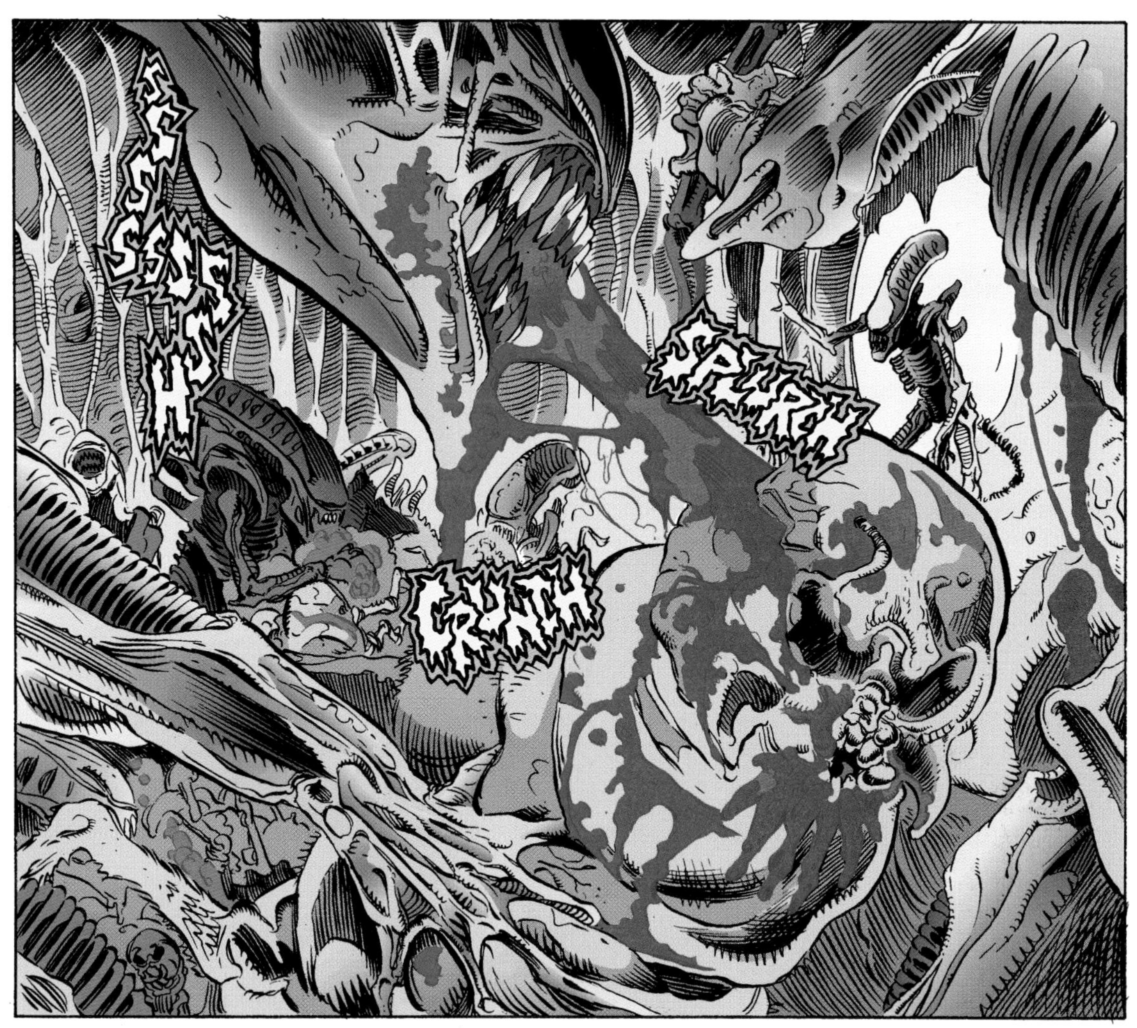
SSSSSHH
SPLURCH
CRUNCH

I THINK WE'VE SEEN ENOUGH, JERI.

WHY DON'T WE MOVE ON.
YEAH, WHY DON'T WE?

WHAT'S THE PROBLEM? I MEAN, THIS IS WHY A CAMERA WAS INSTALLED IN JERI'S HEAD; TO RUN VISUAL SECURITY CHECKS.
I DON'T THINK THERE'S ANY NEED TO DO IT DURING FEEDING TIME.

OH, THAT'S NOTHING. WAIT TILL YOU SEE THE HOST BODIES IN THE GESTATION CHAMBER.

LOOK, DR. NORDLING, ANYONE CAN DO THESE VISUAL CHECKS.
WE CAME HERE TO RUN DIAGNOSTICS ON THE MONITORING SYSTEMS THAT DETECT THE SMALLER, INVISIBLE VIOLATIONS OF SECURITY.

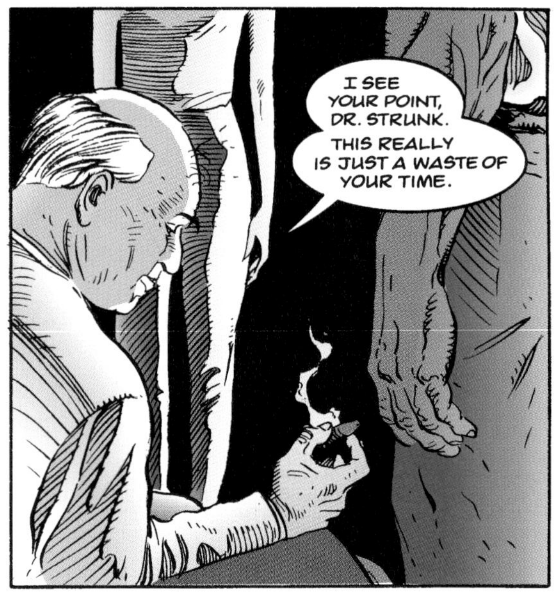
I SEE YOUR POINT, DR. STRUNK.
THIS REALLY IS JUST A WASTE OF YOUR TIME.

LET'S HEAD DOWN TO THE LAB RIGHT NOW AND YOU CAN GET TO WORK. YOUR WIFE CAN START UP HERE.
WE'RE GOING TO NEED A LITTLE HELP.
HEY, THAT'S WHAT ANDROIDS ARE FOR.
LIZZY, HONEY. YOU STAY HERE AND SHOW MRS. STRUNK THE NEW SOFTWARE WE'VE INSTALLED.
YES, DR. NORDLING.
KEEP UP THE GOOD WORK.
IN A FEW MINUTES ...
BASICALLY, THIS PROGRAM ENHANCES OUR ABILITY TO PREDICT STRESS FRACTURES THAT MAY OCCUR IN THE DIVIDING WALL.
THIS IS ACCOMPLISHED BY A RANDOM EMISSION OF ELECTRICAL—
LIZZY?
LIZZY, DOESN'T IT EVER BOTHER YOU?
THE WAY DR. NORDLING TOUCHES YOU, DOESN'T THAT... BOTHER YOU?

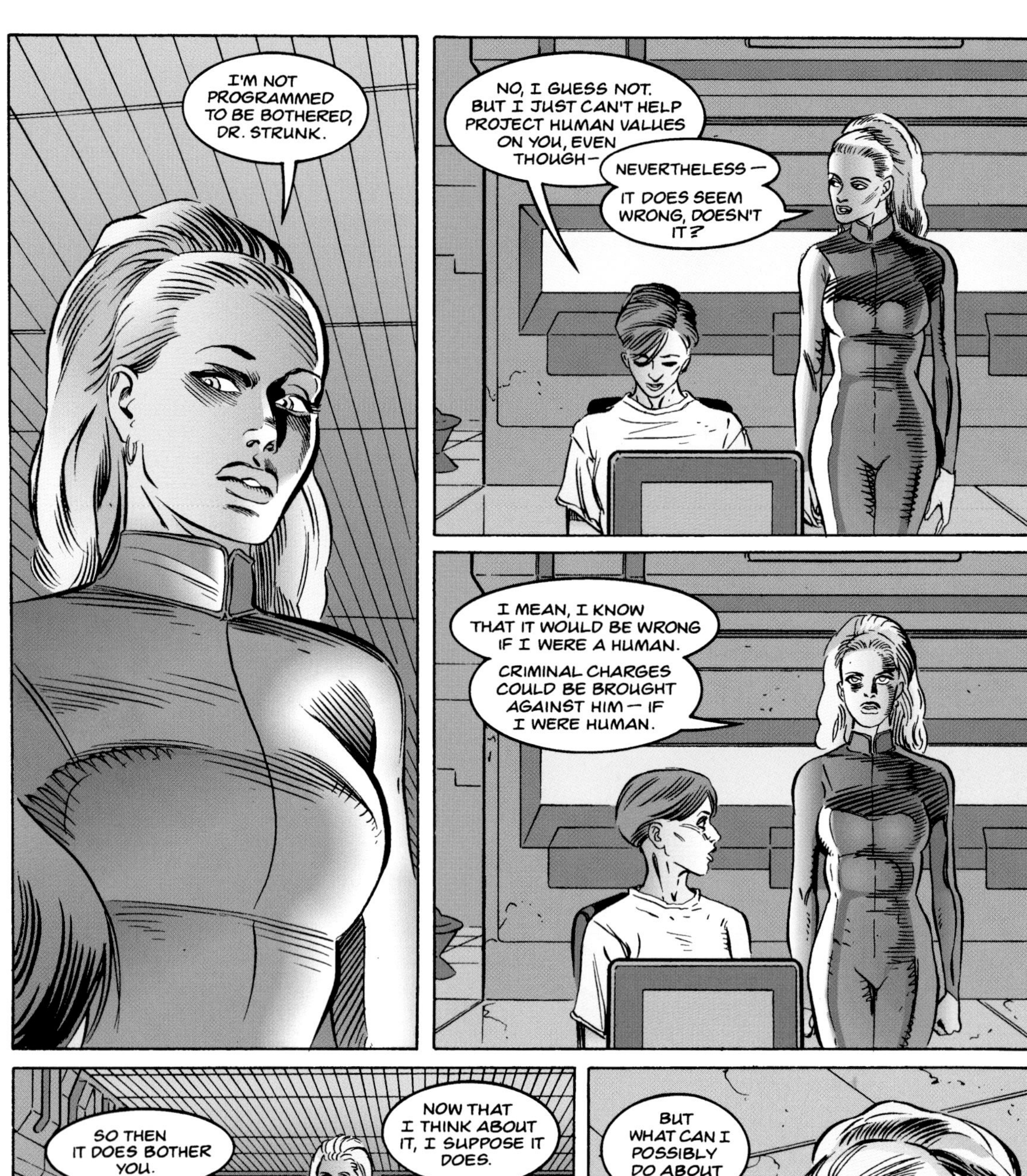
I'M NOT PROGRAMMED TO BE BOTHERED, DR. STRUNK.
NO, I GUESS NOT. BUT I JUST CAN'T HELP PROJECT HUMAN VALUES ON YOU, EVEN THOUGH—
NEVERTHELESS—
IT DOES SEEM WRONG, DOESN'T IT?
I MEAN, I KNOW THAT IT WOULD BE WRONG IF I WERE A HUMAN.
CRIMINAL CHARGES COULD BE BROUGHT AGAINST HIM—IF I WERE HUMAN.

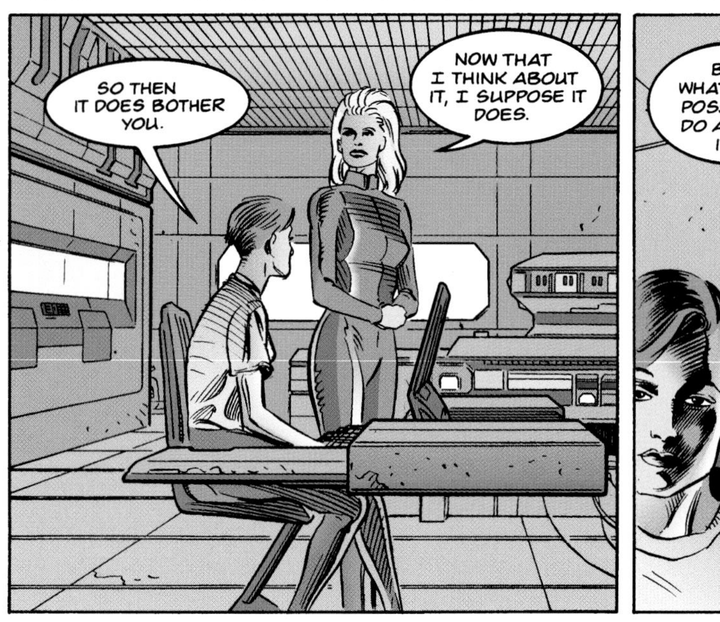
SO THEN IT DOES BOTHER YOU.
NOW THAT I THINK ABOUT IT, I SUPPOSE IT DOES.

BUT WHAT CAN I POSSIBLY DO ABOUT IT?

EEEEEEE
♫ MMMM-MMMM ♪
EXCUSE ME, DR. NORDLING.
HMMM, YES?
WHAT IS IT?
NO ONE HAS SHOWN UP-TO-HELP-
WHAT THE HELL ARE YOU DOING?
OH, IT'S NOT SO BAD.
LET ME SHOW YOU SOMETHING.

YOU SEE THAT LITTLE TAB THERE?
UH-HUH.

WELL YOU SEE, THAT'S A VITAL-SIGNS MONITOR.
IT TRACKS USEFUL INFORMATION WHILE I APPLY VARIOUS STRESSORS TO THE CREATURE.
STRESSORS... LIKE CUTTING OFF AN ARM?

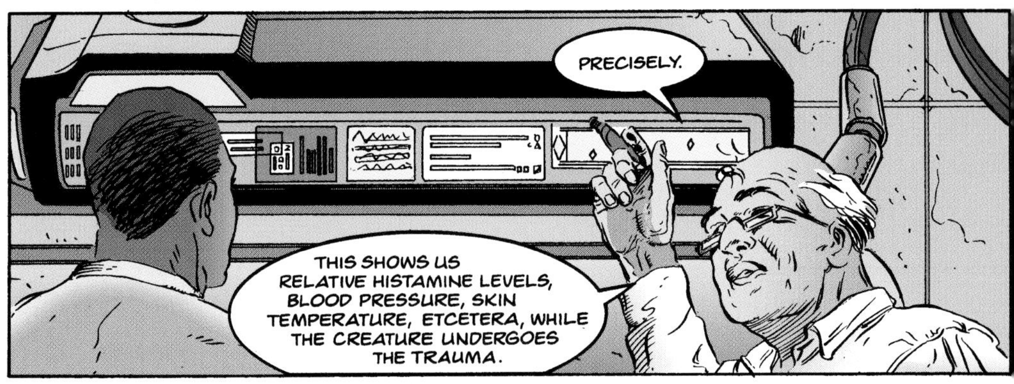
PRECISELY.
THIS SHOWS US RELATIVE HISTAMINE LEVELS, BLOOD PRESSURE, SKIN TEMPERATURE, ETCETERA, WHILE THE CREATURE UNDERGOES THE TRAUMA.

THE BOTTOM OF THE CAGE IS MOSTLY NEUTRAGEL, NEUTRALIZING THE ACID IN THE SPILT BLOOD.
MAKING IT POSSIBLE TO STUDY IT FOR POST-TRAUMATIC WHITE COUNT AND PLATELET LEVELS.

OF COURSE, I'M PUTTING THIS ALL IN HUMAN TERMS, BUT THESE ARE APPROPRIATE PARALLELS FOR WHAT WE SEE IN THE CREATURES' PHYSIOGNOMY.
AND THIS IS RELEVANT TO YOUR WORK?

OH, VERY MUCH SO, DR. STRUNK.
ALL THIS IS KEY TO MY UNDERSTANDING OF THEIR IMMUNITY SYSTEM—
A "SYSTEM" I'M TRYING TO "BEAT."
I SEE. SO WHAT DO YOU DO WITH THE BODIES?
BODIES? WELL, MOST OF THEM LIVE.
THEY HAVE REMARKABLE RECOVERY AND SURVIVAL SKILLS. TRUE, THEY ARE RELEASED INTO A BENIGN ENVIRONMENT. THEIR HIVE—
AH, BUT THAT'S ANOTHER STUDY AL-TOGETHER.
YOU KNOW, YOU SEEM SO DIFFERENT TODAY. I MEAN, YESTERDAY YOU WERE SO INFORMAL, ALMOST—
CRUDE?
WELL...
AHH, IT'S ALL RIGHT. I KNOW WHO I AM. BUT YOU SEE, THAT'S MY PERSONAL LIFE, AND *THIS* — THIS IS SCIENCE.
AND I AM, AFTER ALL, A SCIENTIST.

WELL, ANYWAY, I STILL NEED SOME HELP WITH THAT.
OH, RIGHT. THAT'S WHY YOU CAME TO SEE ME IN THE FIRST PLACE.
TELL YOU WHAT, PHIL— I CAN CALL YOU PHIL, RIGHT? LET'S HEAD OVER TO DR. PAYNE'S AND SEE WHAT'S WHAT.

"DR. PAYNE?"
"THAT'S WHAT I CALL HIM. YOU'LL SEE WHY."

HEY, DOC!
DAMN.

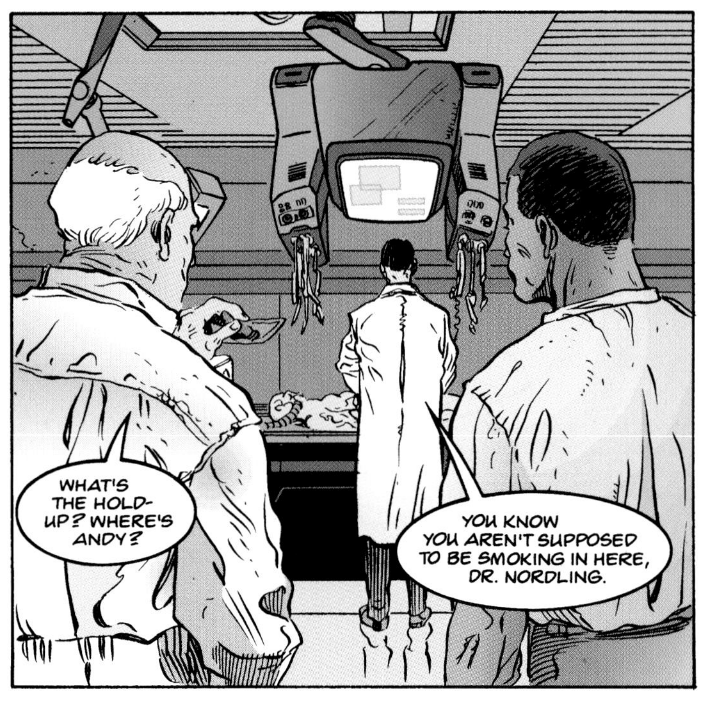
WHAT'S THE HOLD-UP? WHERE'S ANDY?
YOU KNOW YOU AREN'T SUPPOSED TO BE SMOKING IN HERE, DR. NORDLING.

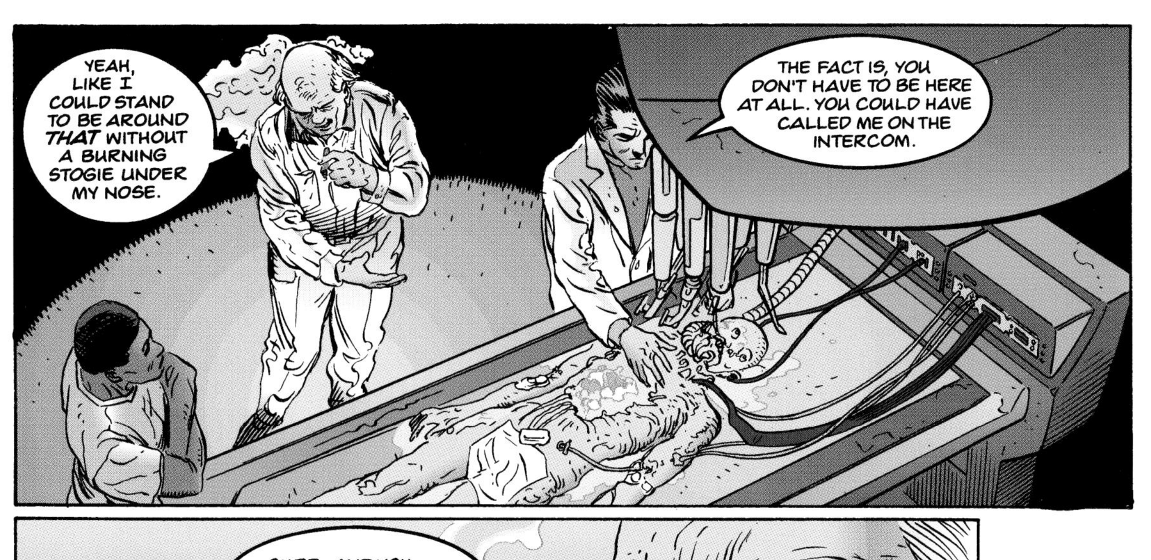
YEAH, LIKE I COULD STAND TO BE AROUND *THAT* WITHOUT A BURNING STOGIE UNDER MY NOSE.
THE FACT IS, YOU DON'T HAVE TO BE HERE AT ALL. YOU COULD HAVE CALLED ME ON THE INTERCOM.

SURE. AND YOU COULD IGNORE ME, JUST LIKE YOU ALWAYS DO.
SO WHAT'S THE STORY WITH ANDY? ALL YOU HAD TO DO WAS REPLACE AN EYE.

BELIEVE IT OR NOT, YESTERDAY'S HIVE DISASTER HAS ME A BIT BACKED UP.

LOOK, WE REALLY NEED ANDY IN THE LAB. COULD YOU HURRY IT UP?
UNLIKE THE OTHERS, I WASN'T PROGRAMMED TO RESPOND TO YOUR CONCERNS, DR. NORDLING.
MY SOLE FUNCTION HERE IS TO EFFECT REPARATIONS ON MY FELLOW SYNTHETICS.

ALL RIGHT, YOU SMART-MOUTHED BASTARD. FUN'S OVER.
NOW YOU GET ANDY OUT HERE AND POP A NEW EYE INTO HIS HEAD, OR I'LL BURN YOUR EYES RIGHT THE *#@ OUT OF YOURS!
DR. NORDLING, WHAT THE HELL HAS GOTTEN INTO YOU!?
AW, COME OFF IT! IT'S NOT LIKE HE'S HUMAN, FOR GOD'S SAKE.
DON'T EXPEND YOUR ENERGIES DEFENDING ME, DR. STRUNK.
WHAT!?
IT WAS A NICE GESTURE ON YOUR PART, BUT THE FACT IS, DR. NORDLING WOULD NEVER HARM ME, LEAST OF ALL MY EYES.
YOU SEE, ONLY I CAN REPAIR ALL OF THESE DAMAGED SYNTHETICS.
WITHOUT ME, THIS FACILITY WOULD SHUT DOWN IMMEDIATELY.
I KNOW DR. NORDLING WOULDN'T WANT THAT.

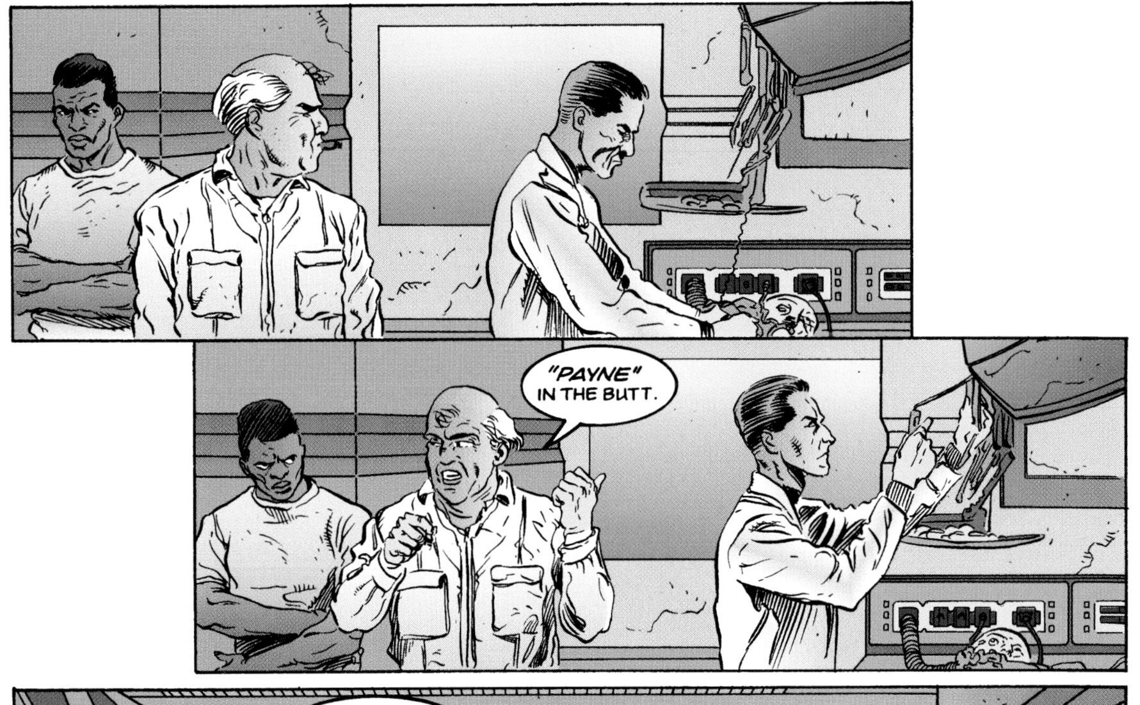
"PAYNE" IN THE BUTT.

AHH, FINALLY, SOME MOVEMENT!
COME ON. WE'LL ROUND UP JERI. HE'LL BE ABLE TO HELP YOU.

NO HE WON'T.
WHAT!
AN ARM WAS MISSING FROM ONE OF LAST NIGHT'S CASUALTIES.

SINCE ARMS ARE TAILOR-MADE, I SENT JERI BACK INTO THE HIVE TO FIND IT.
I TOLD HIM THAT IF HE COULDN'T FIND IT IN THE HIVE —

"HE WOULD HAVE TO GO DOWN BELOW."
DEAN.
HEY, DEAN, IT'S JUST ME, SO DON'T SHOOT.
THIS IS NOT RIGHT. DEAN SHOULD BE ON HIS PLATFORM.
HE'S NOT SUPPOSED TO MOVE AROUND ON HIS OWN DOWN HERE. I DON'T LIKE IT.
AH, THERE'S THE ARM.
EASY ENOUGH.
NOW TO GET OUT OF HERE BEFORE—

WHAT ARE YOU DOING? IT'S ME, IT'S JERI!

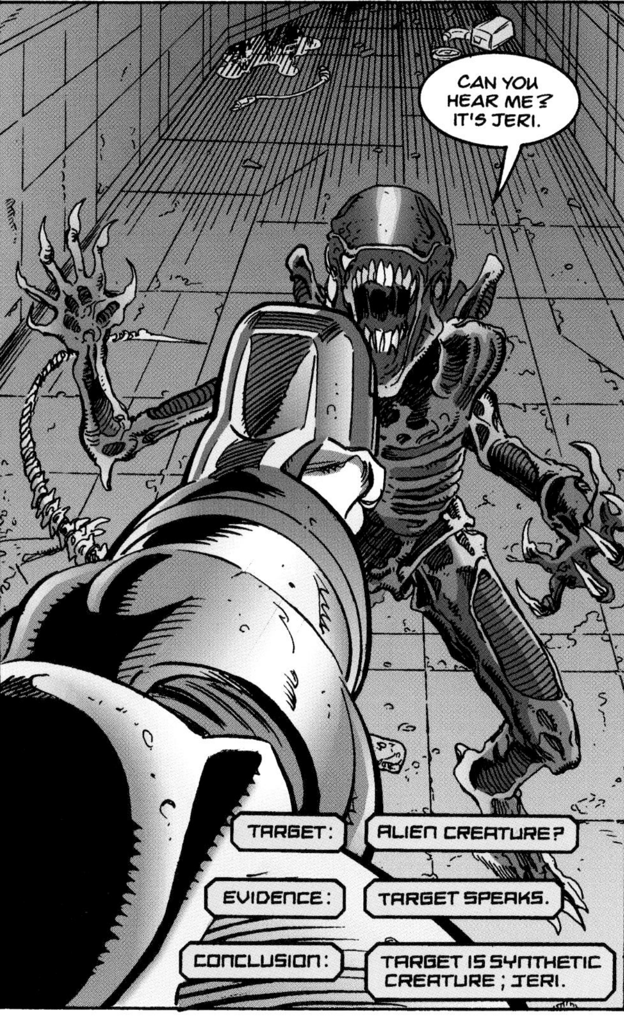
CAN YOU HEAR ME? IT'S JERI.
TARGET:
ALIEN CREATURE?
EVIDENCE:
TARGET SPEAKS.
CONCLUSION:
TARGET IS SYNTHETIC CREATURE; JERI.

IDENTIFICATION CONFIRMED. YOU MAY PASS.
I SHOULD HOPE SO! ARE YOU MAL-FUNCTIONING, OR WHAT!?

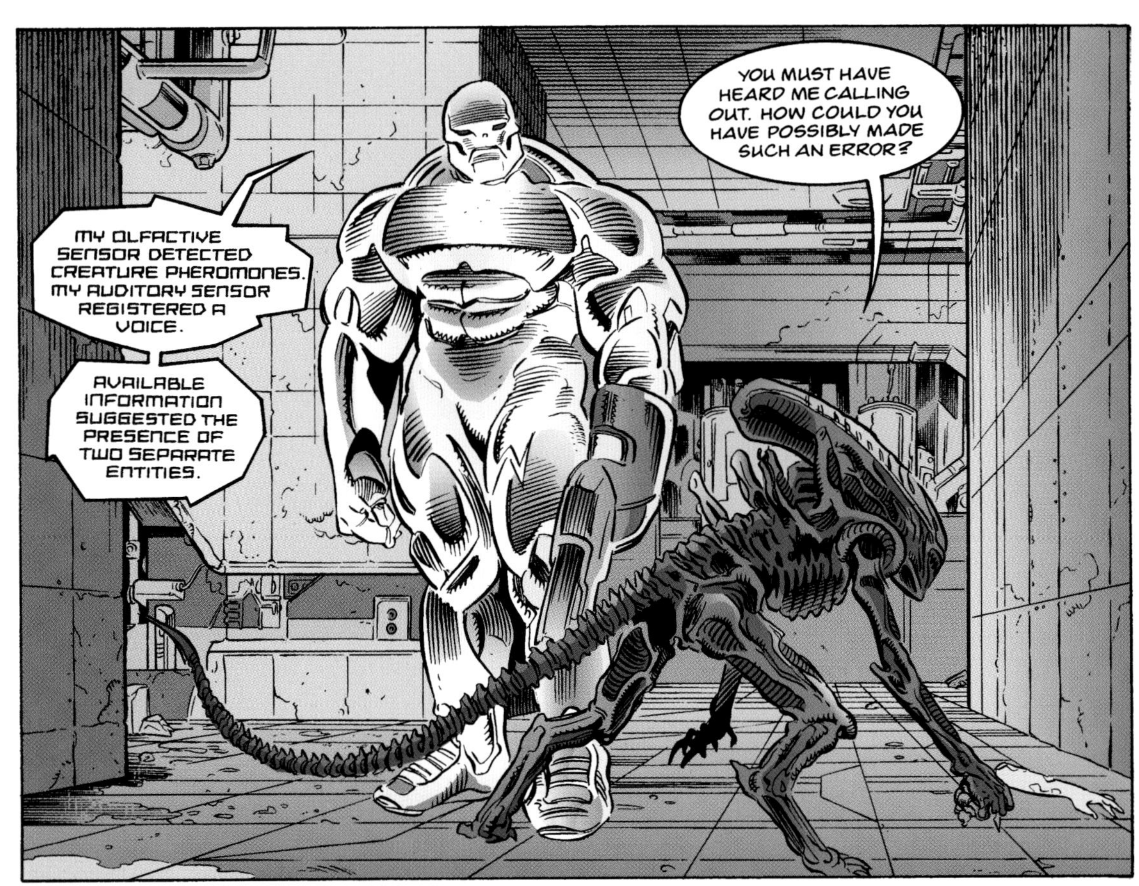
YOU MUST HAVE HEARD ME CALLING OUT. HOW COULD YOU HAVE POSSIBLY MADE SUCH AN ERROR?
MY OLFACTIVE SENSOR DETECTED CREATURE PHEROMONES. MY AUDITORY SENSOR REGISTERED A VOICE.
AVAILABLE INFORMATION SUGGESTED THE PRESENCE OF TWO SEPARATE ENTITIES.

A COMBAT POSTURE WAS REQUIRED UNTIL POSITIVE IDENTIFICATION OF JERI WAS MADE.
NO MALFUNCTION IS INDICATED.
YOU KNOW, DEAN, I'M ALMOST CONVINCED YOU DERIVE A PERVERSE PLEASURE OUT OF STALKING ME.

PER...VERSE.
PERVERSE?

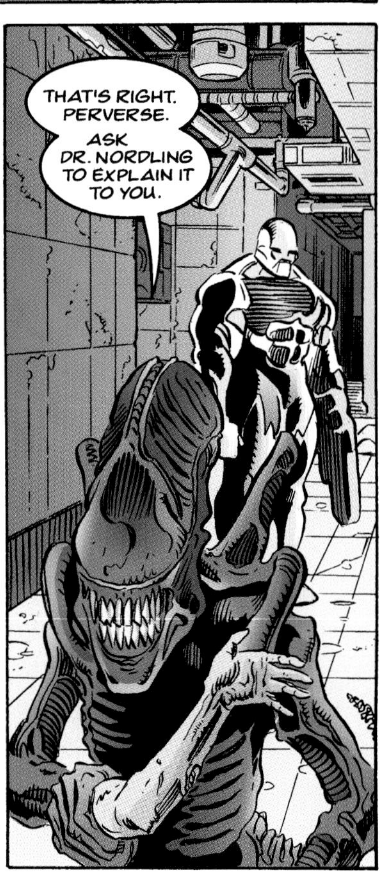
THAT'S RIGHT. PERVERSE.
ASK DR. NORDLING TO EXPLAIN IT TO YOU.

THIS CHAMBER IS ONE LEVEL BELOW US.
WOW! THAT'S A CLEAR PICTURE.

I MEAN, I CAN ALMOST READ THE L.C.D. DISPLAYS ON THE TIMER CLAMPS.
WHICH REMINDS ME, THE CLAMPS ARE NOT MONITORED BY THIS PROGRAM, ONLY THE CHAMBER'S PERIMETER.

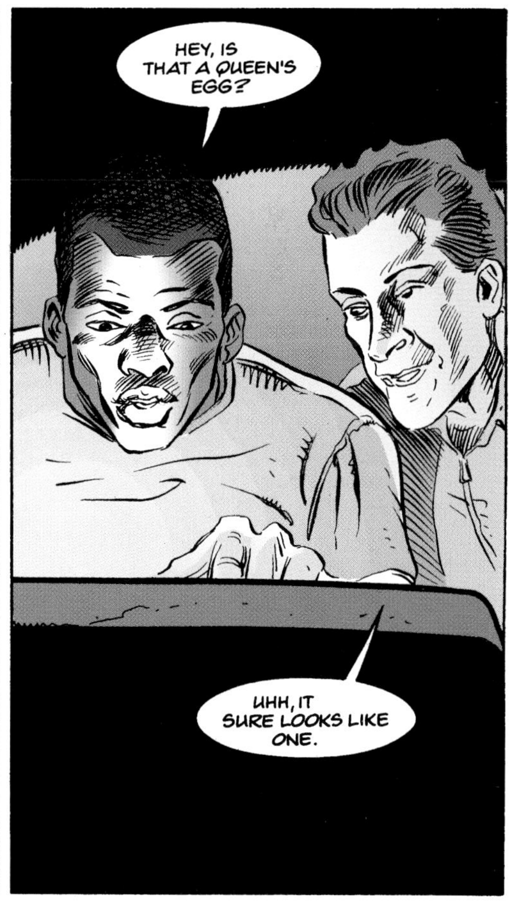
HEY, IS THAT A QUEEN'S EGG?
UHH, IT SURE LOOKS LIKE ONE.

THIS IS A CLEVER PROGRAM. MOST PEOPLE CONSIDER SURVEILLANCE CAMERAS AND SYSTEMIC SECURITY MONITORS AS SEPARATE BRANCHES OF A CHECKS AND BALANCES SYSTEM.
BUT YOU'VE COMBINED THEM INTO A VERY EFFECTIVE UNIT.
ALL OUR PROGRAMS ARE LIKE THAT. I'LL SHOW YOU.
LET'S SUPPOSE WE WANT TO SEE OUR WEAPONS CASE.
TAKE A LOOK AT THE SCREEN NOW.

THAT'S A LOT OF GUNS.

THERE ARE A LOT OF CREATURES HERE.
SINCE THIS IS PART OF THE SECURITY PROGRAM, I TAKE IT NOT EVERYONE HAS ACCESS TO THESE WEAPONS?
NO. THE LOCK TO THE CASE RESPONDS TO THE PALM PRINTS OF ONLY DR. NORDLING AND DR. PAYNE.

OKAY, I CAN SEE WHY NORDLING WOULD QUALIFY, BUT WHY PAYNE?
HE'S THE ONLY SYNTHETIC THAT NEVER GOES INTO THE HIVE, SO THERE'S NO CHANCE OF LOSING HIM IN THERE.

MAKES SENSE.
IF YOU SAY SO. I HAPPEN TO THINK WE ALL SHOULD BE ABLE TO GET THE GUNS, BUT —
EXCUSE ME, DR. STRUNK?

I JUST FINISHED BRIEFING YOUR WIFE UPSTAIRS AND THOUGHT YOU MIGHT NEED SOME HELP, BUT I SEE ANDY IS ALREADY HERE.
YEAH. DR. PAYNE FINISHED UP WITH HIM ABOUT HALF AN HOUR AGO.

I THOUGHT I HEARD YOUR VOICE, LIZZY.
COULD YOU COME BACK HERE... PLEEEASE?

CLICK

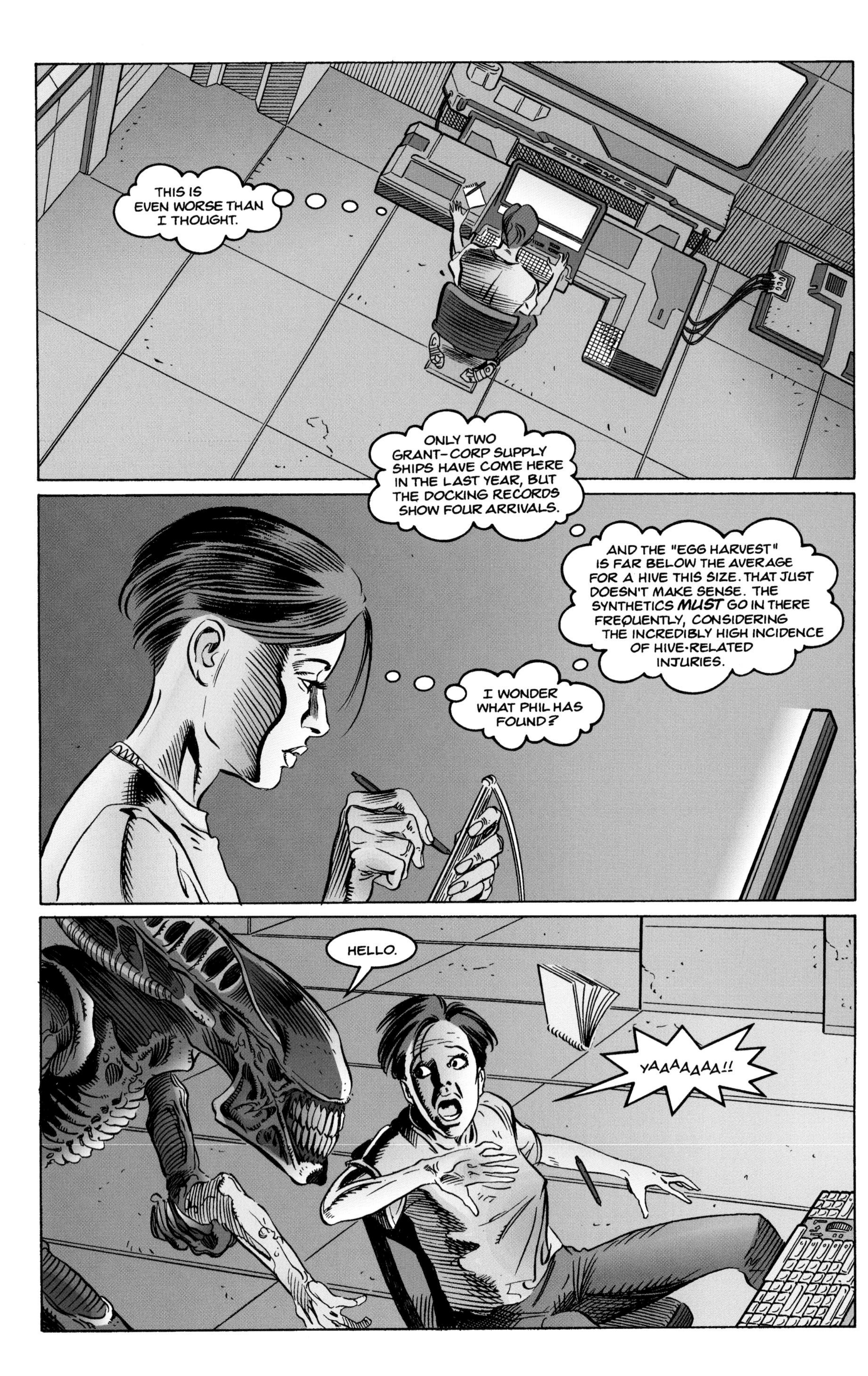
THIS IS EVEN WORSE THAN I THOUGHT.
ONLY TWO GRANT-CORP SUPPLY SHIPS HAVE COME HERE IN THE LAST YEAR, BUT THE DOCKING RECORDS SHOW FOUR ARRIVALS.
AND THE "EGG HARVEST" IS FAR BELOW THE AVERAGE FOR A HIVE THIS SIZE. THAT JUST DOESN'T MAKE SENSE. THE SYNTHETICS MUST GO IN THERE FREQUENTLY, CONSIDERING THE INCREDIBLY HIGH INCIDENCE OF HIVE-RELATED INJURIES.
I WONDER WHAT PHIL HAS FOUND?
HELLO.
YAAAAAAA!!

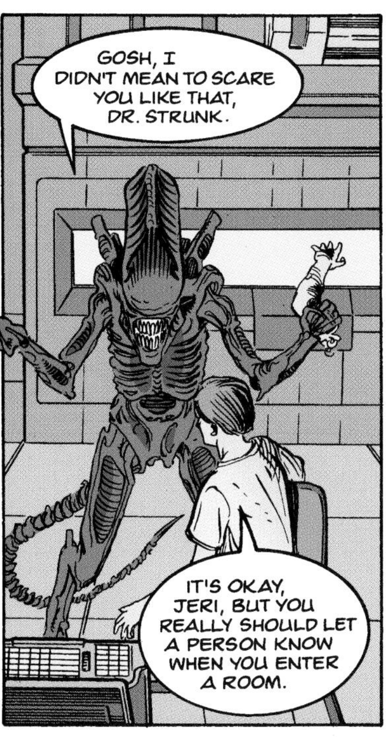
GOSH, I DIDN'T MEAN TO SCARE YOU LIKE THAT, DR. STRUNK.
IT'S OKAY, JERI, BUT YOU REALLY SHOULD LET A PERSON KNOW WHEN YOU ENTER A ROOM.

I DON'T MEAN TO PRY, BUT *THIS* PROGRAM DISPLAYS OUR PRODUCTIVITY FILES.

I THOUGHT YOU WERE SUPPOSED TO BE CHECKING OUR SECURITY SYSTEMS.
YEAH, WELL, YEAH, I AM, BUT UMM... I ACCESSED THESE FILES BY MISTAKE.

BY MISTAKE? THAT WOULD BE VERY DIFFICULT TO DO.
A GLITCH IN THE SYSTEM, MAYBE?
TAK
TAK TAK TAK

PERHAPS. IN WHICH CASE YOU SHOULD LOOK INTO IT.
ANYWAY, *THESE* ARE THE FILES YOU WANT.

UHH THANKS, JERI.
YOU'RE QUITE WELCOME, DR. STRUNK.

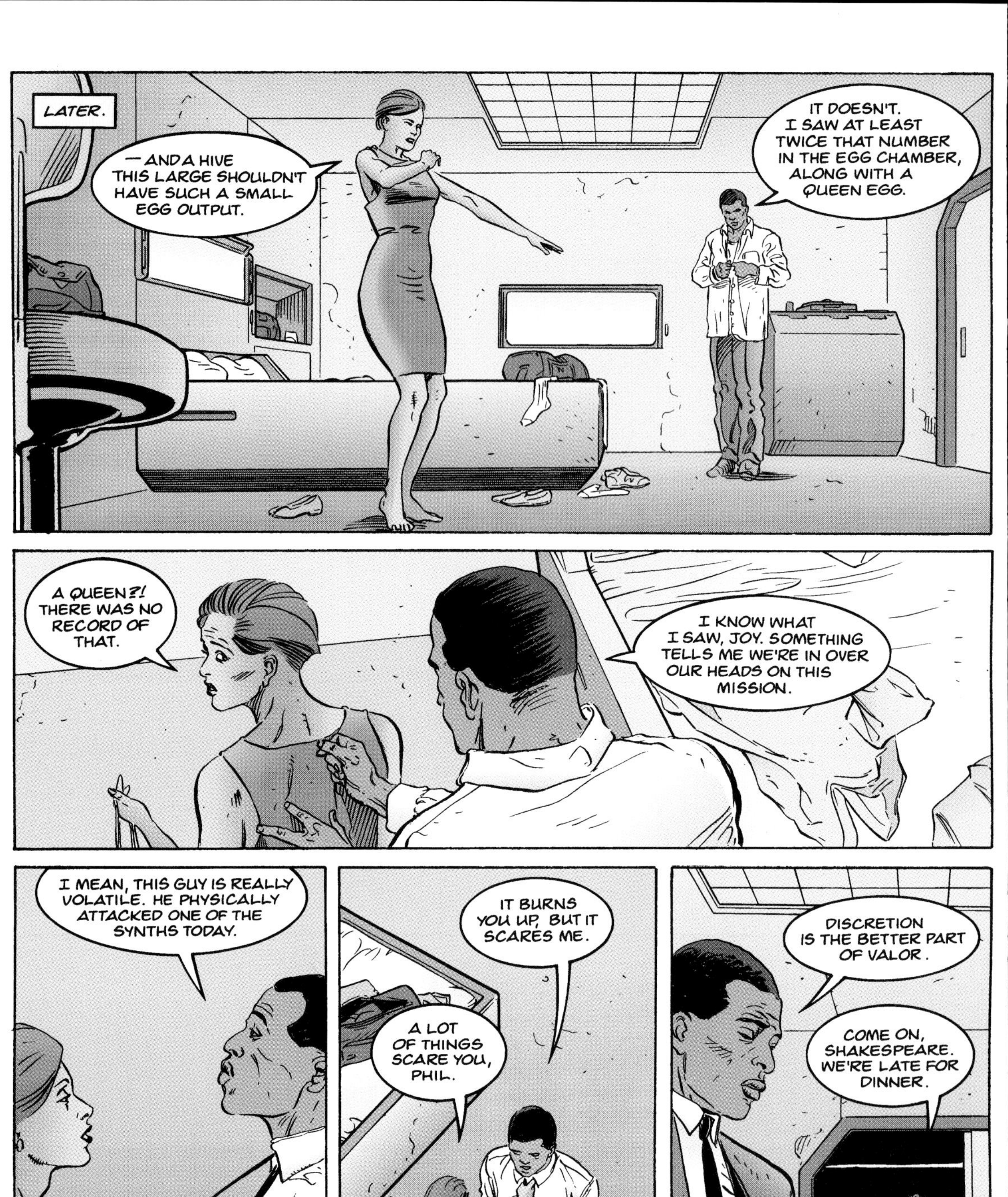
LATER.
—AND A HIVE THIS LARGE SHOULDN'T HAVE SUCH A SMALL EGG OUTPUT.
IT DOESN'T. I SAW AT LEAST TWICE THAT NUMBER IN THE EGG CHAMBER, ALONG WITH A QUEEN EGG.
A QUEEN?! THERE WAS NO RECORD OF THAT.
I KNOW WHAT I SAW, JOY. SOMETHING TELLS ME WE'RE IN OVER OUR HEADS ON THIS MISSION.

I MEAN, THIS GUY IS REALLY VOLATILE. HE PHYSICALLY ATTACKED ONE OF THE SYNTHS TODAY.
THE WAY HE TREATS THOSE ANDROIDS BURNS ME UP.

IT BURNS YOU UP, BUT IT SCARES ME.
A LOT OF THINGS SCARE YOU, PHIL.

DISCRETION IS THE BETTER PART OF VALOR.
COME ON, SHAKESPEARE. WE'RE LATE FOR DINNER.

THANK YOU, JERI.

NO. NO MORE FOR ME. I THINK I'VE ALREADY HAD ENOUGH.
YES, DR. STRUNK.

NOT BAD FOR A SPACE MEAL, EH?
I MEAN, SURE, WE'RE EATING RE-HYDRATED BEEF AND GRAVY—
BUT THE WINE IS VERY REAL.
HEH HEH HEH.
GEE, YOU TWO ARE AWFULLY QUIET.

FEELING A BIT DOWN, IS THAT IT?
SAY, MAYBE YOU'D LIKE TO SEE JERI SMOKE ANOTHER ONE OF THESE?
NO WE WOULDN'T! IN FACT, DR. NORDLING, I DON'T LIKE THE WAY YOU TREAT THE SYNTHETICS.
IT'S ABSOLUTELY UNCONSCIONABLE.
EASY.
THEY MAY NOT BE HUMANS, BUT THEY DO HAVE DIGNITY—
THAT IS, UNTIL THEY WORK WITH YOU.
LISTEN, DR. NORDLING I'M SORRY—
NO!
I'M THE ONE WHO IS SORRY.
YOUR WIFE IS RIGHT. MY BEHAVIOR HAS BEEN TERRIBLE.
I'VE BEEN ACTING LIKE THIS FOR SO LONG, I DON'T EVEN THINK ABOUT IT ANYMORE.
IT TOOK AN OUTSIDE OBSERVER TO WAKE ME UP TO WHAT I'M DOING.
JU-JUST SO'S YOU'RE NOT MAD...
I-I DON'T FEEL WELL.

I MAY ACT AS IF IT DOESN'T BOTHER ME —
BUT THE TRUTH IS, LIVING OUT HERE FOR SO LONG WITHOUT ANOTHER HUMAN AROUND CAN DRIVE A GUY, WELL —

A LITTLE CRAZY.

A LITTLE CRAZY.
PHIL!

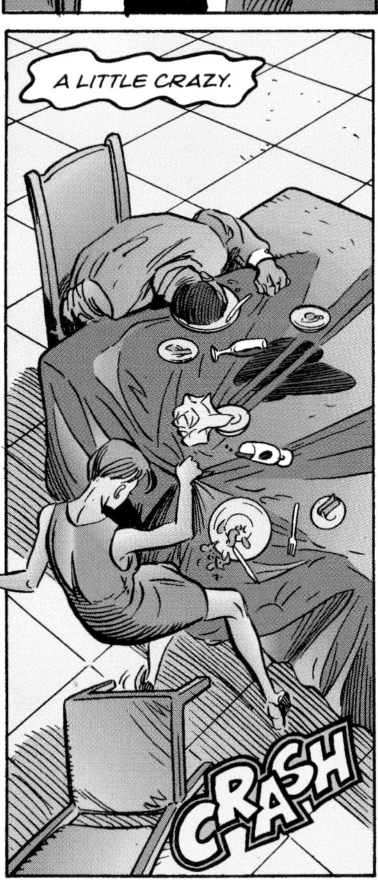
A LITTLE CRAZY.
CRASH

A LITTLE CRAZY.
PHIL.

A LITTLE CRAZY.
PHIIILLL...

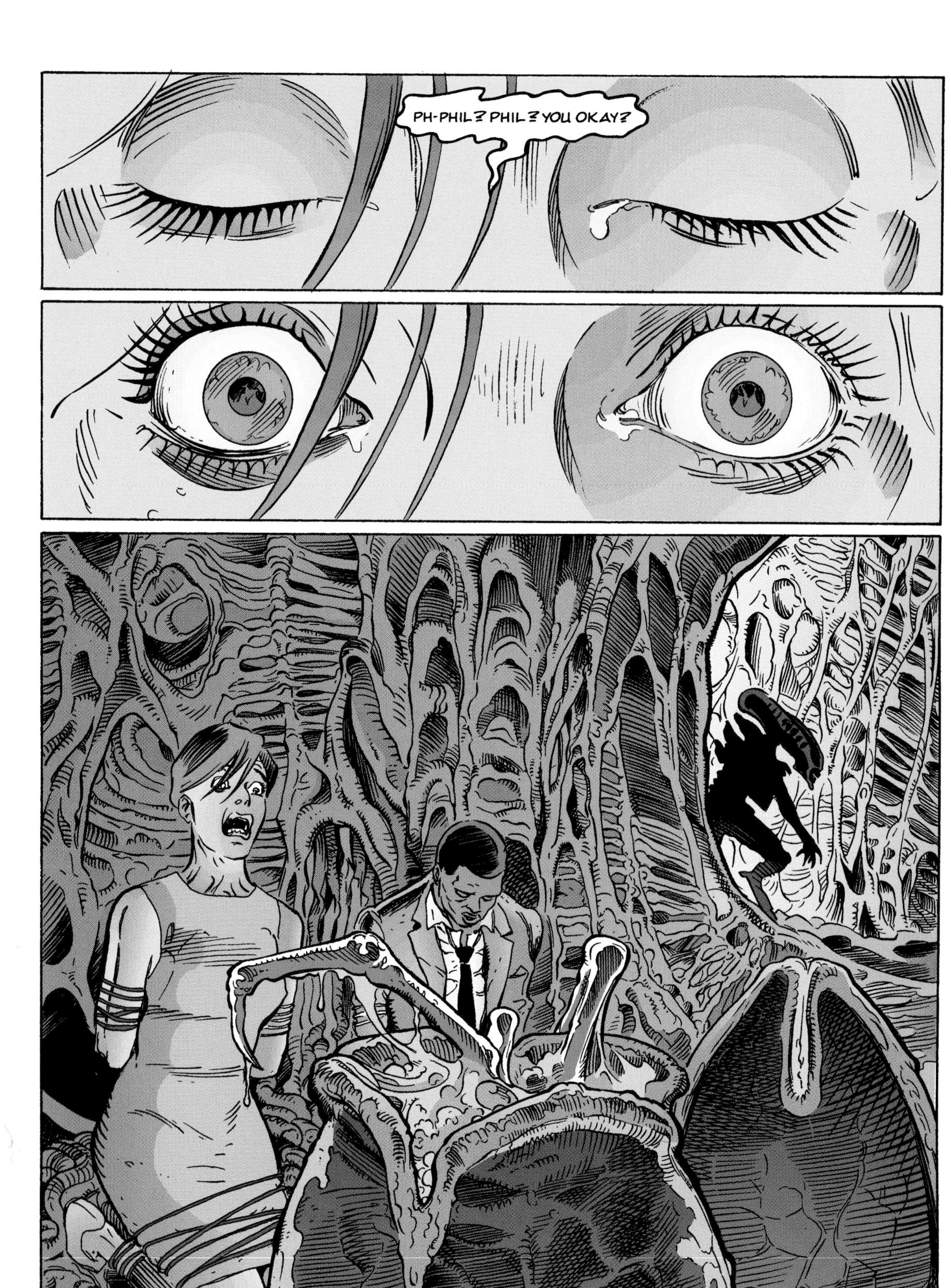
PH-PHIL? PHIL? YOU OKAY?

NORDLIIING!!!

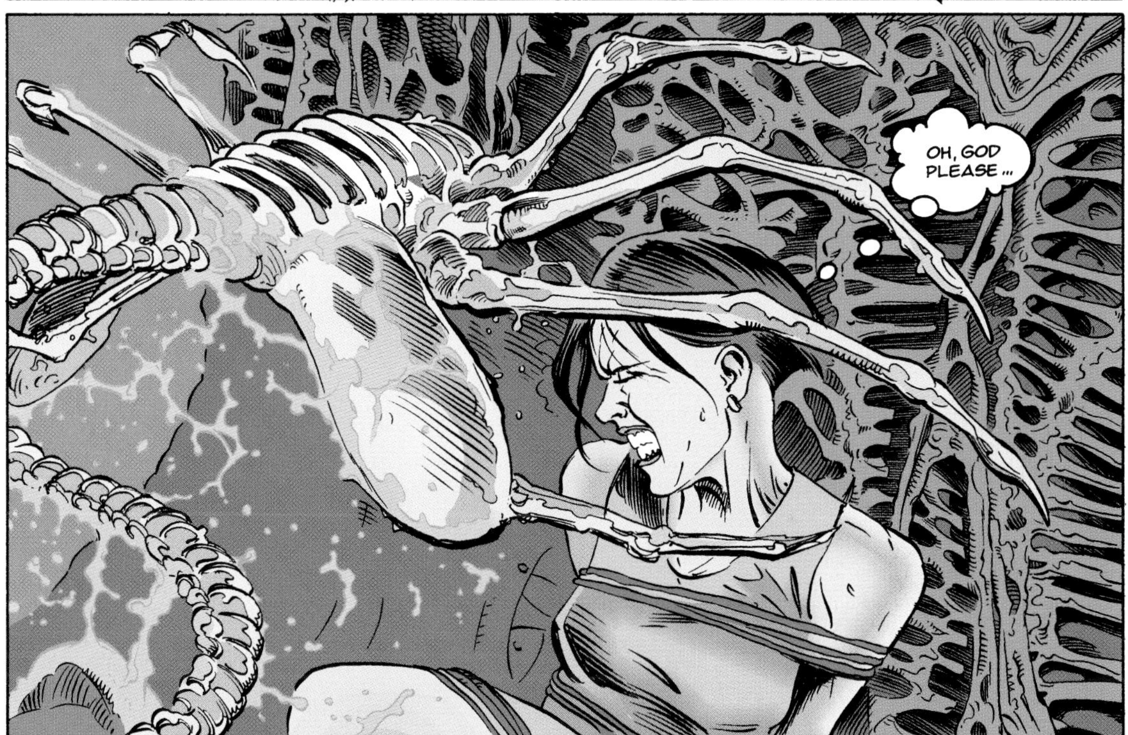
OH, GOD PLEASE...

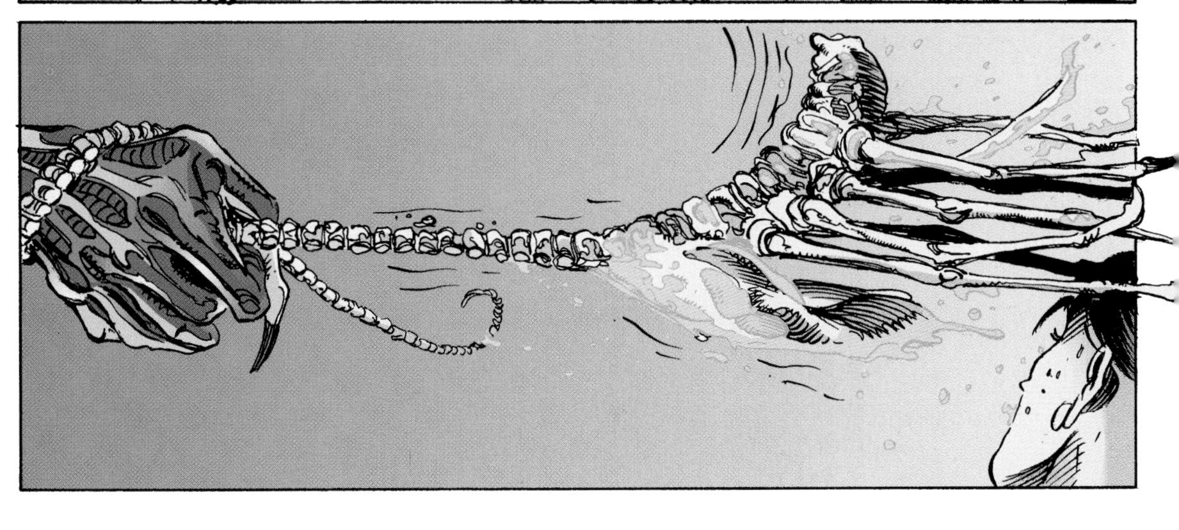

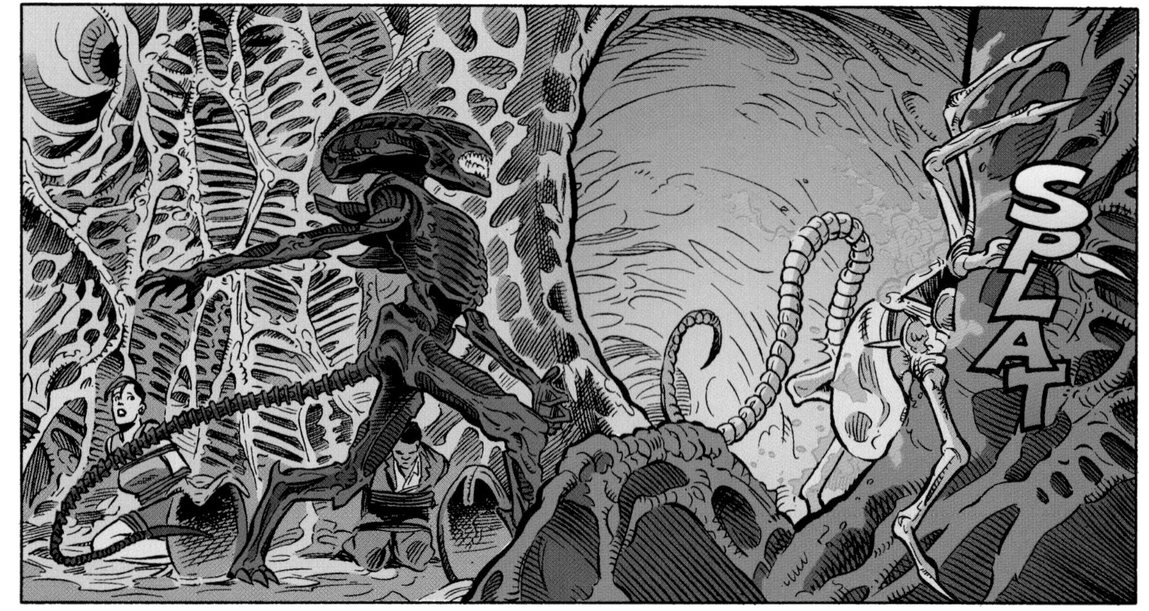
SPLAT

YOU MUST BE IN A STATE OF SHOCK, DR. STRUNK, BUT I'LL HAVE TO ASK YOU TO GATHER YOUR WITS.

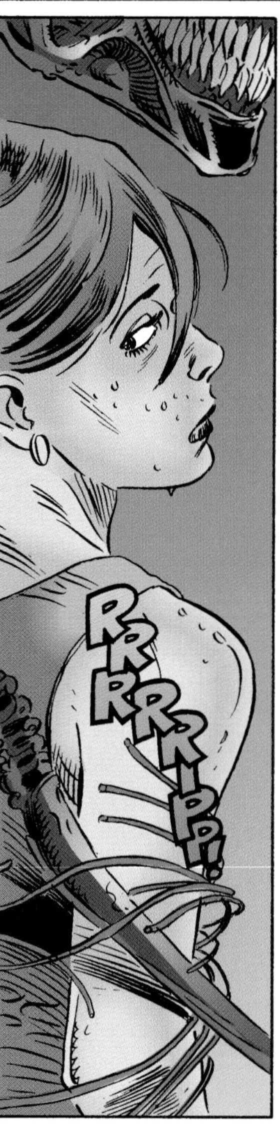
RRRRRRIPP!

YOU SEE, ONCE THE MATURE CREATURES SMELL THE ALARM PHEROMONES GIVEN OFF BY THAT LARVA I JUST KILLED, THEY'LL COME HERE IN DROVES.

HOLD ON A SECOND, BUDDY!
NOT NOW, DOCTOR, THERE ISN'T ANY TIME!

THEN YOU'D BETTER FIND SOME TIME, 'CAUSE I WANT SOME ANSWERS — **NOW!**

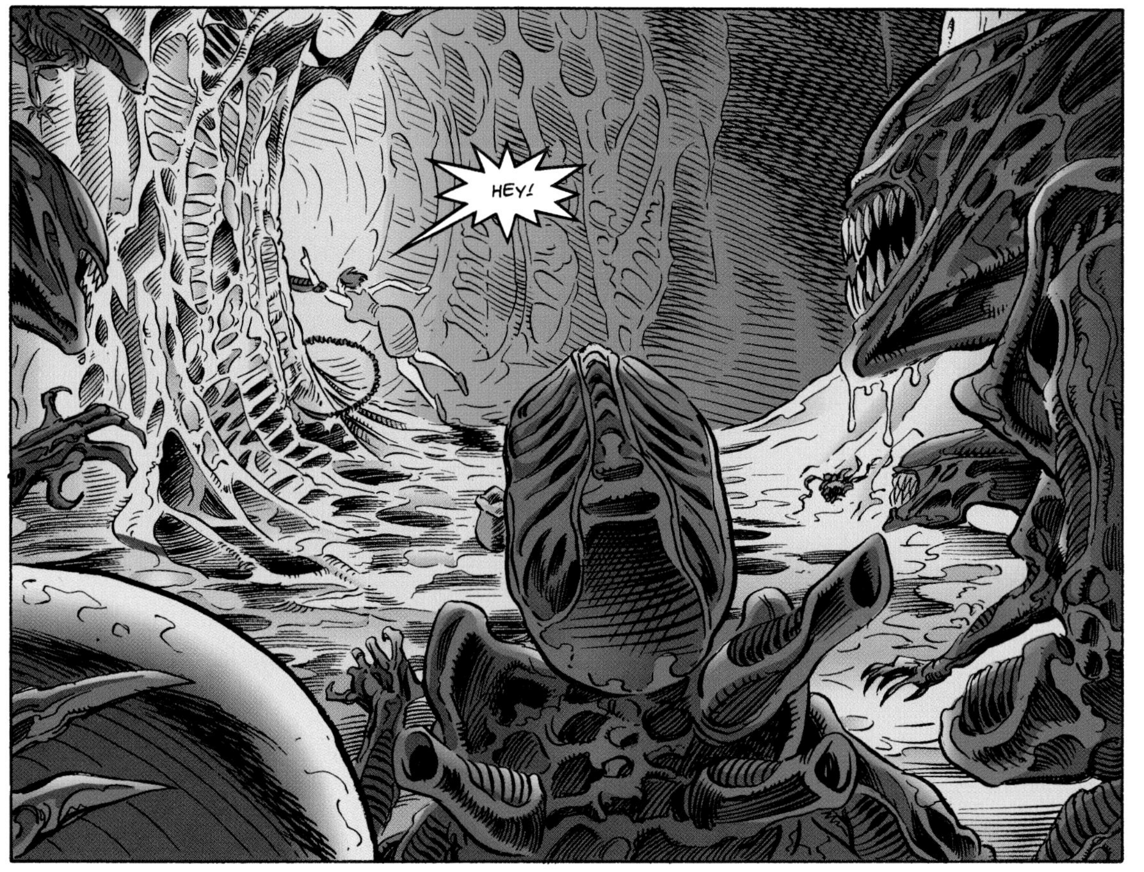
HEY!

WHOOA!
BEEP
BEEP
BEEP
KLAAANG

DR. STRUNK, YOU MAY THINK YOURSELF A STRONG-MINDED INDIVIDUAL—
BUT THE FACT IS, YOU'RE VERY DIFFICULT TO DEAL WITH.
PHIL, HONEY? YOU OKAY?
YEH. FINE.

LOOK, MAYBE I SHOULD BE THANKING YOU, AND MAYBE NOT, BECAUSE NORDLING COULDN'T HAVE PUT US IN THERE HIMSELF.
AN ANDROID HAD TO HAVE DONE IT, AND SINCE YOU WERE SPYING ON ME IN THE MONITOR ROOM, WHY NOT YOU?

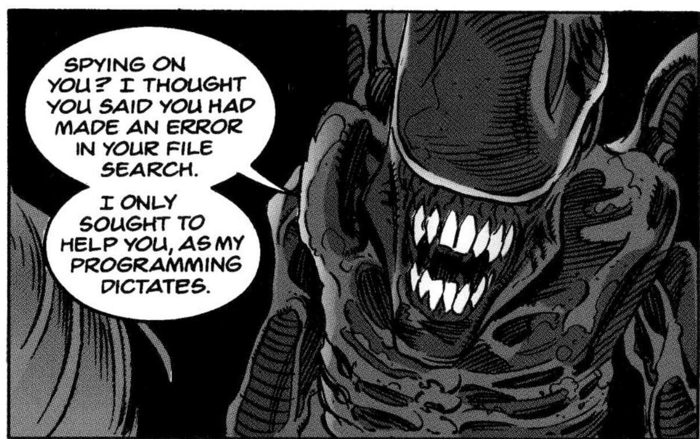
SPYING ON YOU? I THOUGHT YOU SAID YOU HAD MADE AN ERROR IN YOUR FILE SEARCH.
I ONLY SOUGHT TO HELP YOU, AS MY PROGRAMMING DICTATES.

WHICH IS WHY I COULD NOT HAVE PUT YOU IN THE HIVE. MY PRIME DIRECTIVE FORBIDS ME FROM EVER PLACING A HUMAN IN ANY DANGER.
IN FACT, I MUST ALWAYS AID HUMANS, AS I'VE JUST DEMONSTRATED.
ASSUMING YOU'RE OKAY, THAT DOESN'T CHANGE THE FACT THAT NORDLING DID NOT PUT US IN THAT HIVE HIMSELF.
CLEARLY, THIS "HUMANS FIRST" PROGRAMMING HAS BEEN ALTERED IN ONE, OR MORE, OF THE SYNTHETICS.

MY GUESS IS, NORDLING DID SOME "CYBER-SURGERY TO ACHIEVE THAT END.
HOLD ON A SECOND.

NORDLING'S BRILLIANT, NO DOUBT ABOUT THAT, BUT OUR FILES SHOW HIS EXCLUSIVE FIELD IS BIOCHEMISTRY.
OUR FILES DON'T KNOW EVERY-THING.

TRUE ENOUGH, BUT I LEARNED THIS MORNING IN THE SYNTH REPAIR LAB THAT CYBERNETICS ISN'T NORDLING'S BAG.
HE COULDN'T HAVE REPROGRAMMED A SYNTH ON HIS OWN.

HE WOULD'VE NEEDED SOME HELP.
HELP. NOW THERE'S A DAMN GOOD IDEA.
JERI, IF YOU REALLY WANT TO PROVE YOU'RE ONE OF THE "GOOD GUYS," FIND US SOME MORE HELP.

"BECAUSE I THINK WE'RE GOING TO NEED ALL WE CAN GET."

LOOK, I KNOW YOU'RE THE ONLY ONE, BESIDES NORDLING, WHO CAN GET INTO THE WEAPONS CASE. WE NEED YOUR HELP.
I CAN'T DO IT.
WHY NOT?
IF I GET YOU THOSE WEAPONS, YOU'LL USE THEM TO HURT, MAYBE KILL, DR. NORDLING.
THAT WOULD BE IN VIOLATION OF MY PROGRAMMING.
THAT BASTARD TRIED TO KILL US!!
I RECOGNIZE THAT, BUT YOU MUST UNDERSTAND, VOLITION DOES NOT ENTER INTO THIS. I AM TRULY ***UNABLE*** TO COMPLY WITH YOUR REQUEST.
LOOK, ALL WE WANT IS TO GET OUT OF HERE. WHAT IF WE PROMISE NOT TO HURT—
JOY, FORGET IT.
CAN WE POSSIBLY BREAK INTO THAT WEAPONS CASE?
NO. IT WAS BUILT TO WITHSTAND AN ATTACK BY THE CREATURES.
BUT PERHAPS I CAN MAKE ANOTHER SUGGESTION.

NOT TOO FAR AWAY...
AND YOU'RE SURE THAT'S A QUEEN EGG?
OF COURSE I'M SURE.

YEAH, WELL, I GUESS YOU WOULD BE.
LET'S GET DOWN TO IT.
ZZZZIIP

YOU KNOW, DR. NORDLING, IT'S A GOOD THING FOR YOU WE'RE FRIENDS.
IS THAT SO?
I MEAN, YOU AIN'T GOT MUCH SECURITY HERE.
SOME GUYS, ONCE THEY GOT WHAT THEY WANTED, WELL, SOME OF 'EM MIGHT TRY TO FIND A WAY AROUND PAYING YOU.

INDEED THEY MIGHT. I AM A FORTUNATE MAN TO HAVE SUCH A FRIEND.
AREN'T I A FORTUNATE MAN, DEAN?
FOR-TU-NATE.
WHAT THE FRIG!?
MR. CHAUT, MEET DEAN.
HERE'S THE CASH. JUST LIKE YOU WANTED. GO AHEAD AND COUNT IT.
COUNT IT? DON'T BE RIDICULOUS. IF A MAN CAN'T TRUST HIS FRIENDS, WHO CAN HE TRUST?

BY THE WAY, I HAVE SOMETHING FOR YOU, TOO.
OH, NO! YOU REALLY DON'T HAVE TO GIVE ME ANYTHING.
WELL, IT'S REALLY MORE A GIFT TO MYSELF.

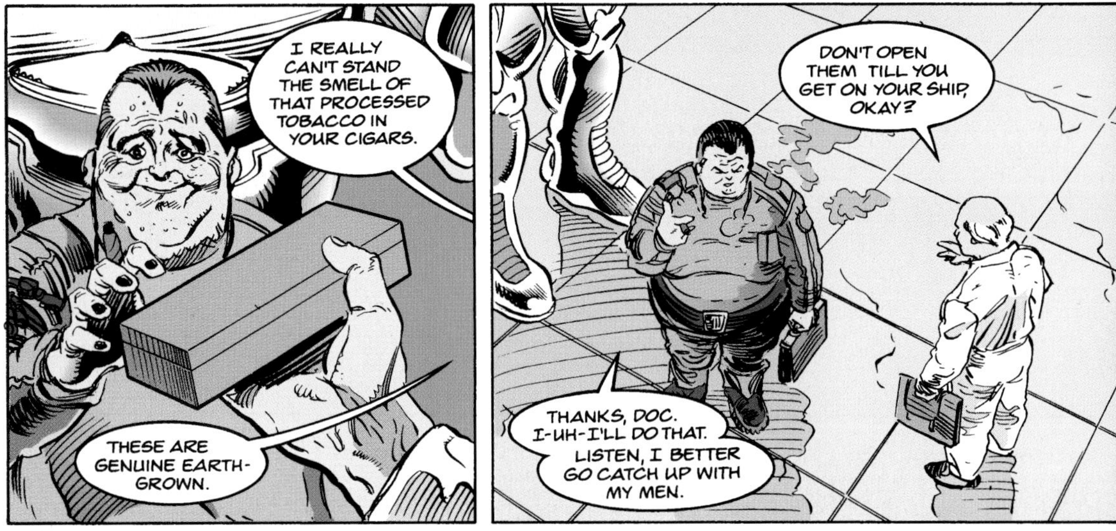
I REALLY CAN'T STAND THE SMELL OF THAT PROCESSED TOBACCO IN YOUR CIGARS.
THESE ARE GENUINE EARTH-GROWN.
DON'T OPEN THEM TILL YOU GET ON YOUR SHIP, OKAY?
THANKS, DOC. I-UH-I'LL DO THAT.
LISTEN, I BETTER GO CATCH UP WITH MY MEN.

THANKS AGAIN. SEE YOU ON THE NEXT TRIP, OKAY?
NICE MEETING YOU, DEAN.
REAL NICE.

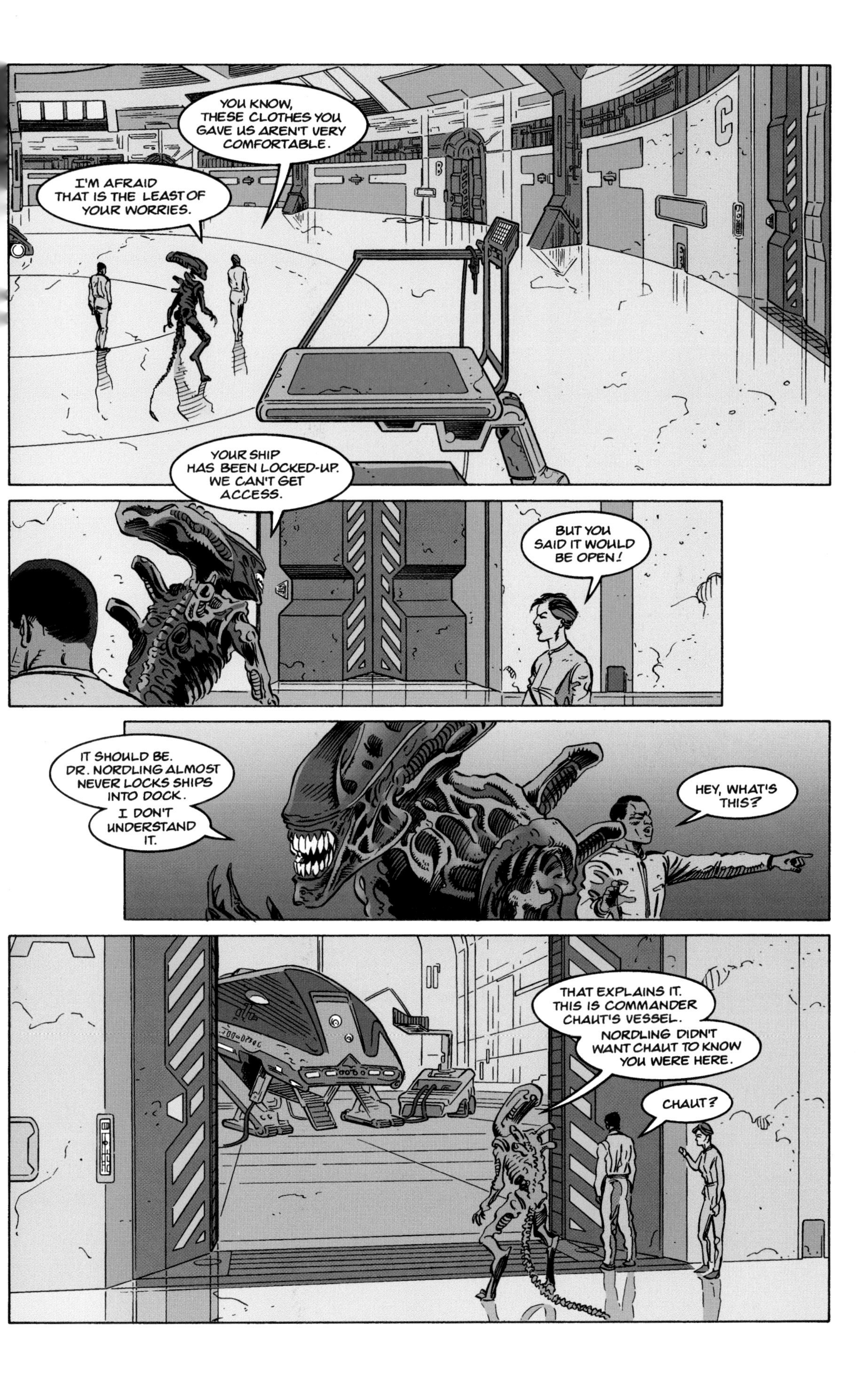
YOU KNOW, THESE CLOTHES YOU GAVE US AREN'T VERY COMFORTABLE.
I'M AFRAID THAT IS THE LEAST OF YOUR WORRIES.
YOUR SHIP HAS BEEN LOCKED-UP. WE CAN'T GET ACCESS.
BUT YOU SAID IT WOULD BE OPEN!
IT SHOULD BE. DR. NORDLING ALMOST NEVER LOCKS SHIPS INTO DOCK.
I DON'T UNDERSTAND IT.
HEY, WHAT'S THIS?
THAT EXPLAINS IT. THIS IS COMMANDER CHAUT'S VESSEL.
NORDLING DIDN'T WANT CHAUT TO KNOW YOU WERE HERE.
CHAUT?

DON'T YOU KNOW HIM? GRANT-CORP SENDS HIM HERE PERIODICALLY TO PICK UP SOME OF THE CREATURES' EGGS.
WHAT ARE YOU TALKING ABOUT? GRANT-CORP DOESN'T PICK UP EGGS.
OH MY GOD! DON'T YOU SEE IT, PHIL?
NORDLING IS SELLING THE EGGS ON THE BLACK MARKET!
OF COURSE. THAT'S WHY ALL THOSE EXTRA EGGS I SAW IN THE CHAMBERS WEREN'T RECORDED IN THE LOGS.
HE'S PROBABLY SELLING RESEARCH TOO, WHICH WOULD EXPLAIN SOME OF HIS EXTREME METHODS.
SO... CHAUT DOESN'T WORK FOR GRANT-CORP?
NO. HE'S A SMUGGLER, AND PROBABLY WORSE. WE'D BETTER GET MOVING.
WELL, WHAT HAVE WE GOT HERE?

I'VE SEEN THIS SYNTH CREATURE BEFORE — BUT NORDLING NEVER TOLD ME ABOUT YOU.
HE-HE DIDN'T?

LYING S.O.B. TOLD ME HE HAD ONLY ONE GIRL SYNTH HERE.
THANK GOD! HE DIDN'T HEAR US.

MAYBE HE JUST BUILT THIS ONE.
HEH HEH. HE DID A PRETTY GOOD JOB, THEN.

EXCUSE US SIR, BUT WE MUST FINISH CLEANING THE AIR PROCESSORS.

HOLD ON A SECOND!

MY FRIEND MOSE WASN'T HERE WITH ME LAST TIME WHEN NORDLING HAD YOU SMOKE THAT CIGAR FOR US.
HE'S JUST DYING TO SEE YOU DO IT.
PERFECT.
WE HAD BETTER HURRY ALONG, JERI.
YOU KNOW HOW ANGRY DR. NORDLING WOULD BE IF HE FOUND US PLAYING GAMES HERE.

SHE'S RIGHT, COMMANDER CHAUT. I REALLY MUST GO.
OKAY, BUT YOU KEEP THE CIGAR. CALL IT A GIFT.

ALL RIGHT. I'LL STORE IT.

THANK YOU.
THWIP!

WOW. D'YOU SEE THAT?! HEY, WHY DID YOU GIVE HIM THAT NICE CIGAR?
YOU DON'T THINK I'D SMOKE IT AFTER THAT THING HAD IT IN ITS MOUTH. 'SIDES, I'M SURE IT'LL PISS NORDLING OFF WHEN HE SEES THAT SYNTH WITH ONE OF HIS "EARTH-GROWN" CIGARS.

ALTHOUGH NOT NEARLY AS MUCH AS WHEN HE FINDS OUT THAT WAS COUNTERFEIT CASH I GAVE HIM.
KEEP IT DOWN, MAN!! THOSE SYNTHS MIGHTA HEARD YOU!

AND WHAT IF THEY DID? THERE'S NO WAY NORDLING CAN STOP US NOW. C'MON.

DID YOU HEAR THAT? COUNTERFEIT!
DON'T WASTE ANY TIME ON NORDLING'S PROBLEMS.

"WE GOT PLENTY OF OUR OWN TO WORRY ABOUT."

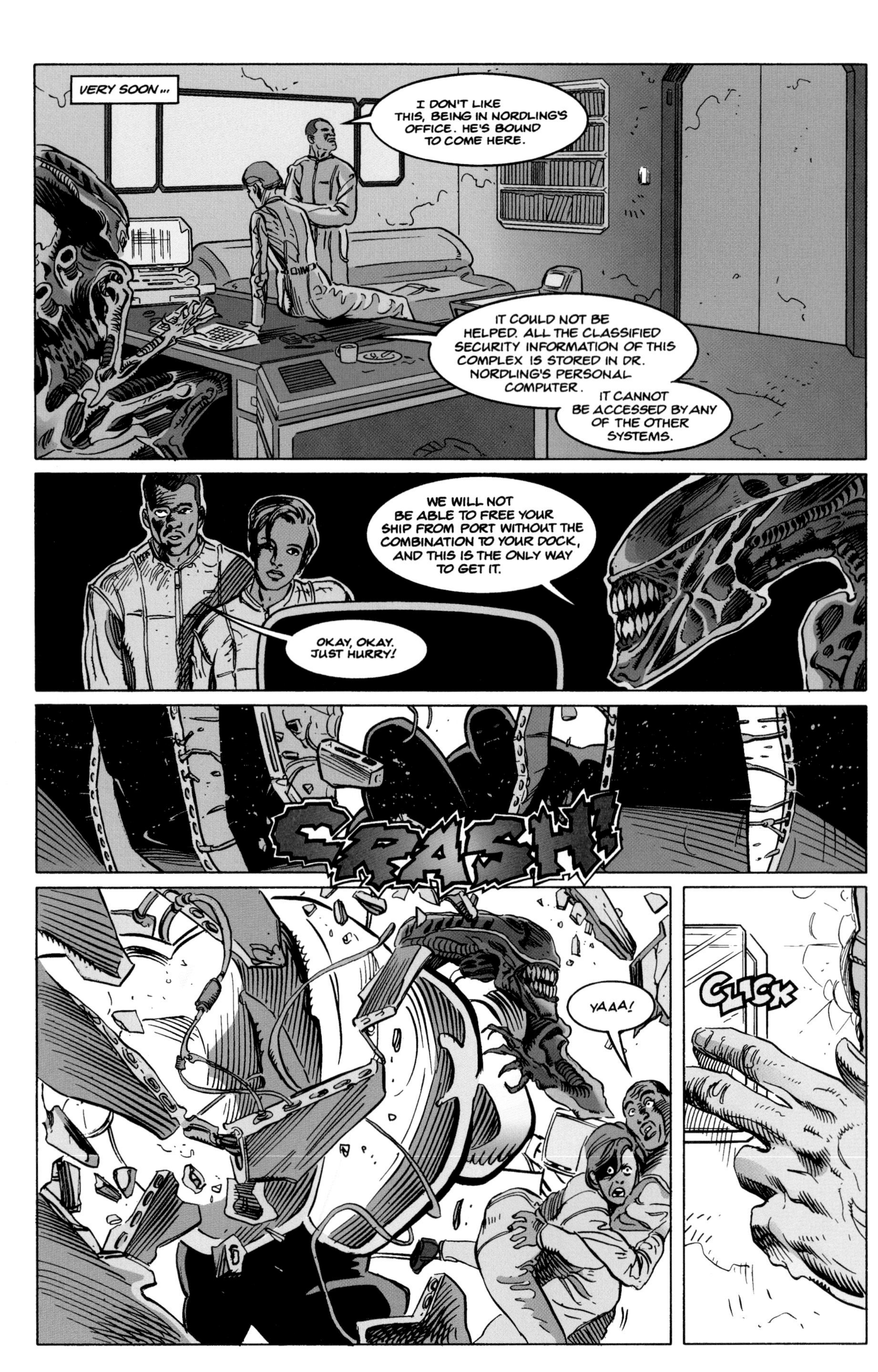
VERY SOON...
I DON'T LIKE THIS, BEING IN NORDLING'S OFFICE. HE'S BOUND TO COME HERE.
IT COULD NOT BE HELPED. ALL THE CLASSIFIED SECURITY INFORMATION OF THIS COMPLEX IS STORED IN DR. NORDLING'S PERSONAL COMPUTER.
IT CANNOT BE ACCESSED BY ANY OF THE OTHER SYSTEMS.
WE WILL NOT BE ABLE TO FREE YOUR SHIP FROM PORT WITHOUT THE COMBINATION TO YOUR DOCK, AND THIS IS THE ONLY WAY TO GET IT.
OKAY, OKAY. JUST HURRY!
CRASH!
YAAA!
CLICK

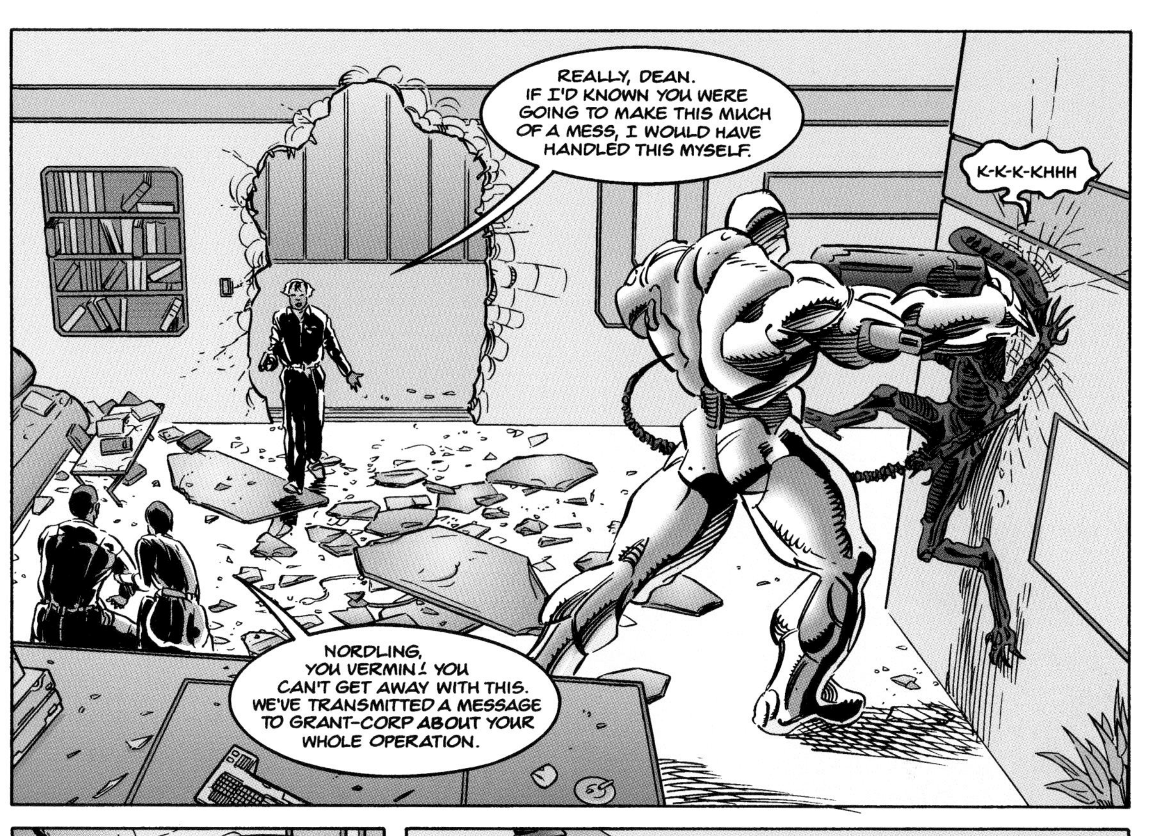
REALLY, DEAN. IF I'D KNOWN YOU WERE GOING TO MAKE THIS MUCH OF A MESS, I WOULD HAVE HANDLED THIS MYSELF.
K-K-K-KHHH
NORDLING, YOU VERMIN! YOU CAN'T GET AWAY WITH THIS. WE'VE TRANSMITTED A MESSAGE TO GRANT-CORP ABOUT YOUR WHOLE OPERATION.

BOY, YOU NEVER QUIT, DO YOU?
LET'S ACCEPT, FOR THE MOMENT, THAT YOU *DID* SEND A MESSAGE. IT'LL BE MONTHS BEFORE ANYONE WILL GET HERE. PLENTY OF TIME FOR ME TO ESCAPE.
BUT OF COURSE, YOU SENT NOTHING.

ALL MESSAGES OFF-PLANET HAVE TO BE AUTHORIZED BY MY PERSONAL I.D. CODE.
WITHOUT IT, YOU CAN'T REACH THE COMMUNICATIONS SUB-STATION IN THIS QUADRANT.

ALL RIGHT, SMART-ASS, YOU GOT US.
BUT YOU ALSO GOT SHAFTED ON YOUR DEAL WITH CHAUT.
THAT'S RIGHT. WE HEARD HIM SAY THE CASH HE GAVE YOU IS COUNTERFEIT.

TELL ME SOMETHING I DON'T KNOW.
YOU-YOU KNEW?
NATURALLY. BIO-DYNAMICS HAD BEEN PLANNING TO BURN ME FOR MONTHS. THEY THINK I CHARGE TOO MUCH.
BUT DON'T WORRY. THEY DIDN'T GET AWAY WITH IT.

"IF YOU HEARD CHAUT TALKING, THEN YOU PROBABLY SAW THAT BOX OF CIGARS I GAVE HIM."
NOW, LET'S TRY ONE OF THESE BABIES OUT.

"EACH CIGAR WAS INJECTED WITH A DORMANT FORM OF A VIRULENT CONTAGION I'VE DEVELOPED.
"IT CAN ONLY BE ACTIVATED BY EXTREME HEAT.

"BUT ONCE ACTIVATED, ITS EFFECTS ARE ALMOST INSTANTANEOUS."
KOFF
KOFF
KOFF
OOOOHH

"I WONDER IF CHAUT WILL FIGURE IT OUT?"
NOO... NOOD... LEEENG-G-G-G...
"FORTUNATELY FOR THOSE GUYS, IT'LL ALL BE OVER IN JUST A FEW MINUTES."

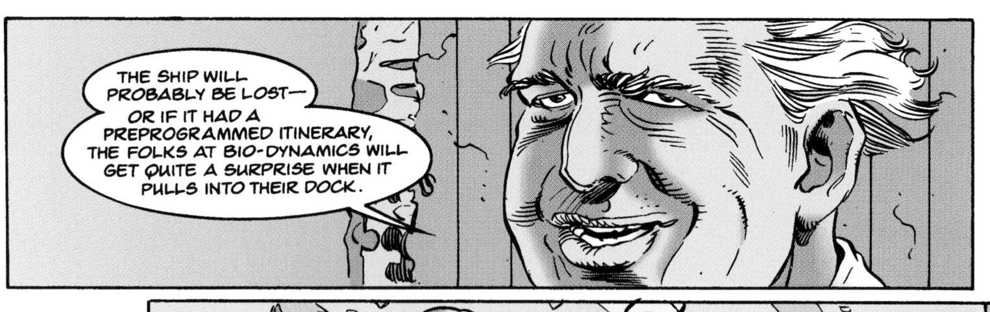
THE SHIP WILL PROBABLY BE LOST—
OR IF IT HAD A PREPROGRAMMED ITINERARY, THE FOLKS AT BIO-DYNAMICS WILL GET QUITE A SURPRISE WHEN IT PULLS INTO THEIR DOCK.

IN ANY CASE, I DON'T THINK THEY'LL EVER TRY TO SCREW ME AGAIN, DO YOU?
I THINK YOU'RE A COLD-BLOODED, LOWLIFE SCUMBAG.

AHH, WHO CARES WHAT YOU THINK.
I SWEAR, IF YOU HADN'T REWIRED THIS GIANT TO DO YOUR BIDDING, I'D RIP YOU LIMB FROM LIMB MYSELF!

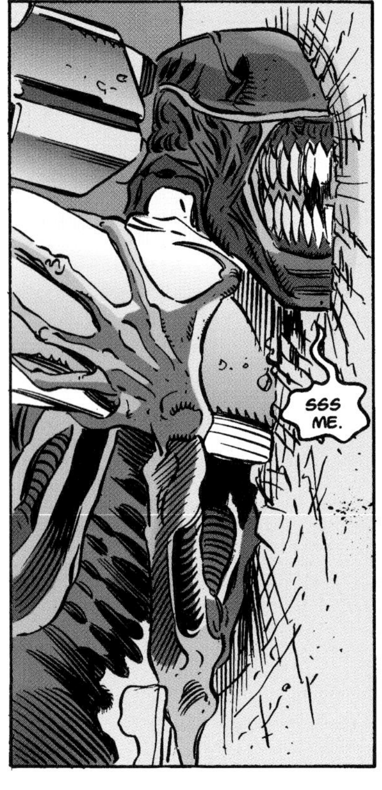
SSS ME.

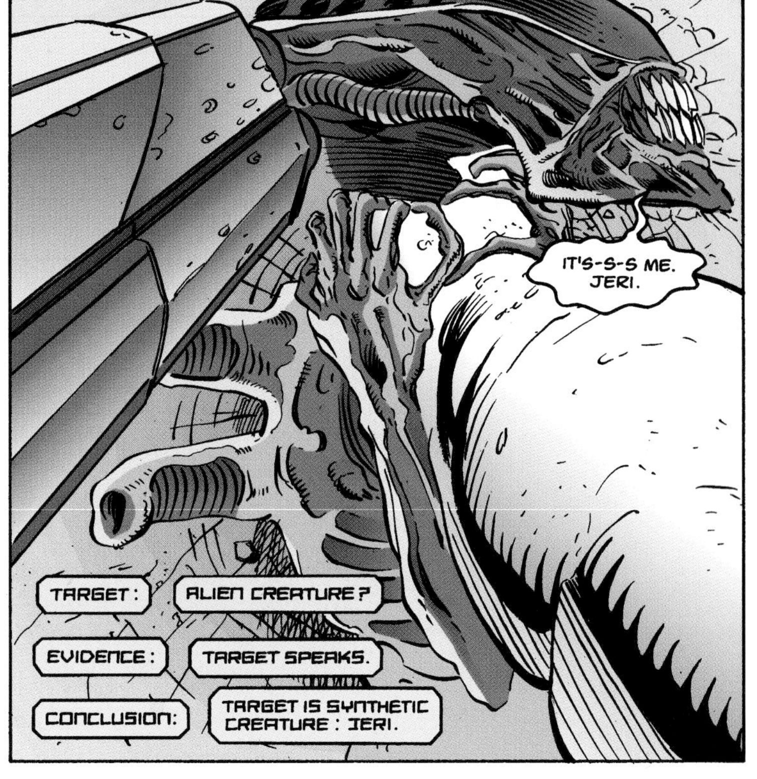
IT'S-S-S ME. JERI.
TARGET:
ALIEN CREATURE?
EVIDENCE:
TARGET SPEAKS.
CONCLUSION:
TARGET IS SYNTHETIC CREATURE: JERI.

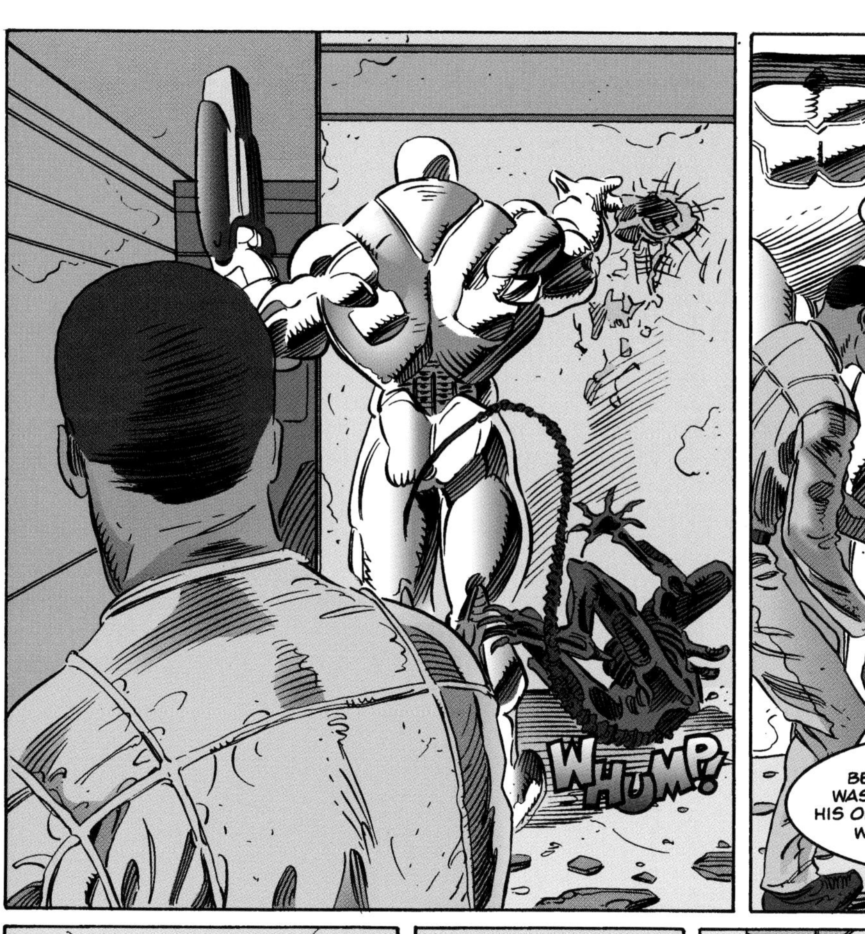
WHUMP!

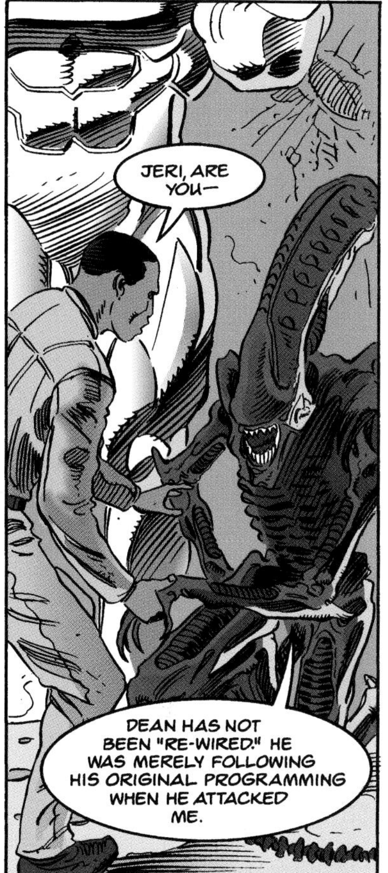
JERI, ARE YOU—
DEAN HAS NOT BEEN "RE-WIRED." HE WAS MERELY FOLLOWING HIS ORIGINAL PROGRAMMING WHEN HE ATTACKED ME.

ARE YOU SURE?
HE RELEASED ME, DIDN'T HE? BESIDES WHICH, IF DR. NORDLING HAD A PLASMA-RIFLE-TOTING ANDROID AT HIS COMMAND—

WHY WOULD HE NEED A HAND GUN?
ALL RIGHT, NOW. JUST WATCH YOURSELVES. I KNOW HOW TO USE THIS.

HAAII!

DON'T EVEN HAVE A ROUND CHAMBERED. I GUESS YOU DON'T KNOW HOW TO USE THIS THING, BUT I DO.
THREE YEARS IN THE MARINES.
SHIK

HOW DO YOU LIKE HAVING A GUN POINTED IN YOUR FACE, HUH PAL!?

YAAAAA!!
CRACK

I DON'T IMAGINE HE LIKES IT VERY MUCH AT ALL, DR. STRUNK.

WHHAK!

WHERE THE HELL HAVE YOU BEEN?
I WAS DESTROYING THE STRUNKS' FILES AND CLOTHES, JUST AS YOU DIRECTED ME TO DO.
WELL, FORGET THAT. JUST GET THEM OUTTA HERE.
OH, PHIL. IS IT--?
IT'S BROKEN ALL RIGHT.

YOU LIED TO ME, YOU--YOU TWISTED FA@#ING MACHINE!
WE'RE FINISHED. WHAT CAN WE POSSIBLY DO AGAINST A KILLER ROBOT?
YOU CAN'T DO ANYTHING, DR. STRUNK.

YOU'RE ONLY HUMAN.

SLAASH

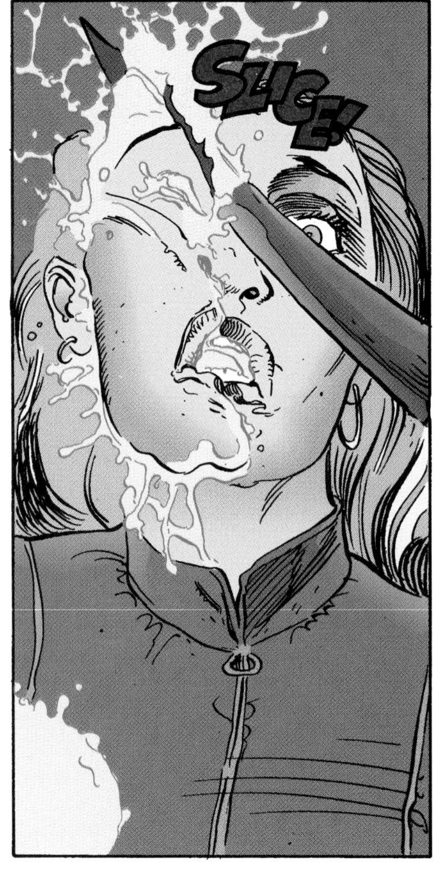
SLICE!

YOU DIRTY BASTARDS! I'LL GET YOU FOR THIS!

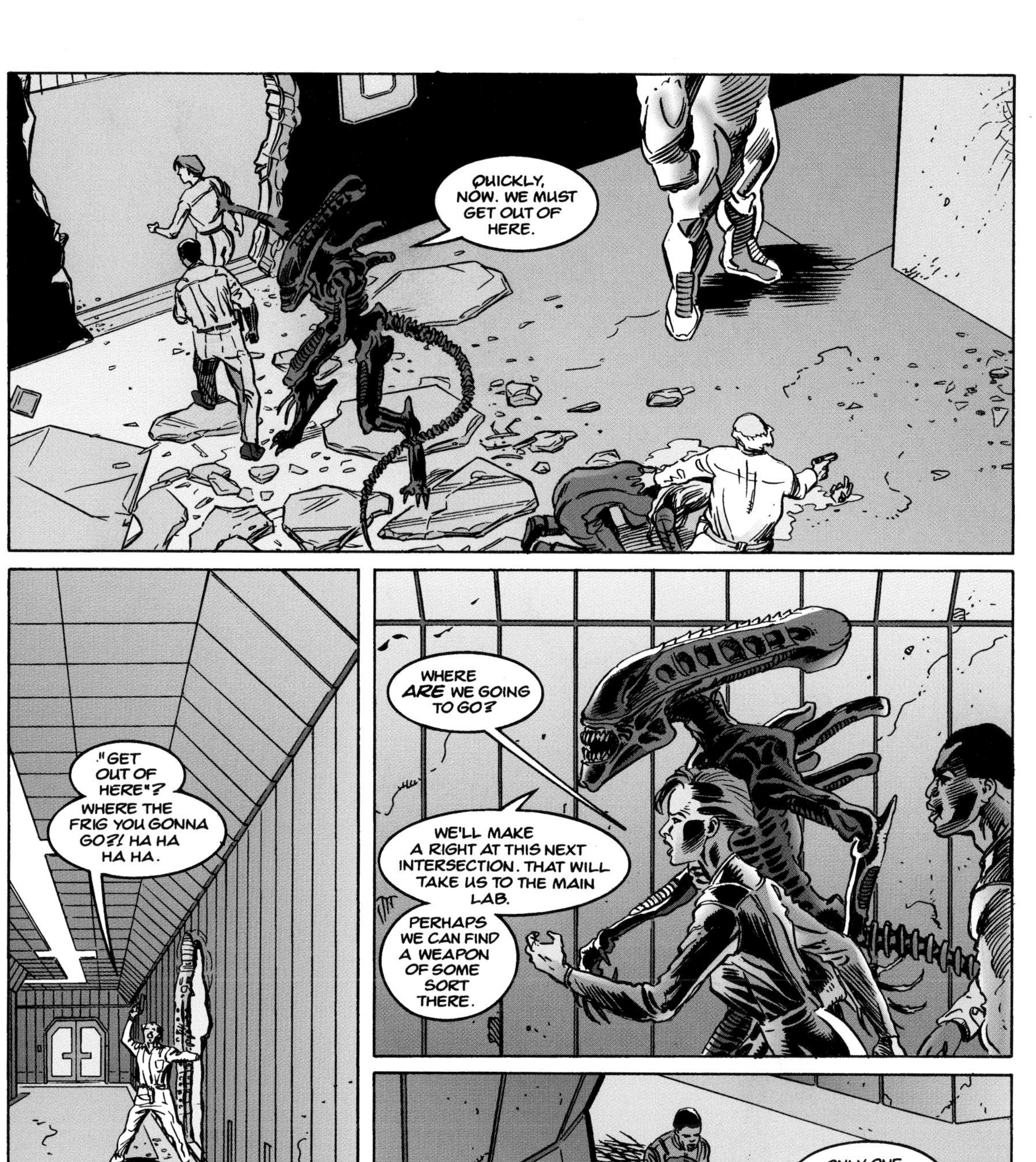
QUICKLY, NOW. WE MUST GET OUT OF HERE.
"GET OUT OF HERE"? WHERE THE FRIG YOU GONNA GO?! HA HA HA HA.
WHERE ARE WE GOING TO GO?
WE'LL MAKE A RIGHT AT THIS NEXT INTERSECTION. THAT WILL TAKE US TO THE MAIN LAB.
PERHAPS WE CAN FIND A WEAPON OF SOME SORT THERE.

ONLY ONE PROBLEM WITH THAT PLAN.
WHAT'S THAT?

WHAT IF SOMEONE GOT THERE AHEAD OF US?

DR. PAYNE! I DON'T UNDER-STAND...

I TH- THOUGHT YOU WERE NEUTRAL.
NO. NOT NEUTRAL.
SHAAK
NOT QUITE.

BLAM
I MAY NOT BE ABLE TO HURT DR. NORDLING, BUT THAT DOESN'T MEAN I LIKE THE MAN, OR WHAT HE'S DOING.
THEN YOU'RE NOT ON NORDLING'S SIDE?
WHAT ARE YOU TALKING ABOUT?! I THOUGHT I EXPLAINED TO YOU--
LIZZY. WHAT ABOUT LIZZY? DR. NORDLING COULDN'T HAVE RE-PROGRAMMED HER BY HIMSELF.
NO... NO, YOU'RE RIGHT.
I HAD SOMETHING TO DO WITH THAT.
BACK WHEN THIS PROJECT STARTED, NORDLING CAME TO ME WITH A *PROBLEM*, AS HE CALLED IT.
HE WANTED TO EXPAND LIZZY'S RESPONSIBILITIES A BIT, SO SHE COULD HELP EASE HIS WORK-LOAD.

"OF COURSE, THIS WAS IN VIOLATION OF LIZZY'S ESTABLISHED FUNCTION PARAMETERS, BUT IT WAS WHAT MY PROGRAM RECOGNIZED AS A REASONABLE REQUEST.
"SO I SHOWED NORDLING HOW TO RESCIND SECURITY CODES AND RE-DEFINE LIZZY'S FUNCTION PARAMETERS.
"HE PICKED UP ON IT RATHER QUICKLY. I HADN'T PLANNED TO TEACH HIM VERY MUCH, BUT HUMANS HAVE A WAY OF SURPRISING YOU-- UH, THAT IS, ME.
"I LAID THE GROUNDWORK, AND HE EXTRAPOLATED THE REST."
IN THAT RESPECT, I'M GUIL--
BLAM
WHAT WAS THAT?!
IN HERE.
WHAT ARE YOU DOING!?!
BOOM
WE'RE PUTTING DR. NORDLING OUT OF BUSINESS.
I'M HEADING DOWN TO THE EGG CHAMBER.
SHHKSW
STOP IT! STOP. THERE ARE VIRUS CULTURES IN THIS LAB.

RELAX, DR. STRUNK. ALL THE SYNTHETICS KNOW EXACTLY WHERE THE VIRUS CONTAINMENT UNITS ARE KEPT AND THEY AREN'T ABOUT TO DAMAGE ANY.
IT'S AGAINST OUR PROGRAMMING TO ALLOW YOU TO COME TO HARM, REMEMBER?

OUR ONLY INTENTION IS TO ELIMINATE NORDLING'S CAPABILITIES TO CONTINUE IN HIS WAYS.
AND MAYBE GET HIM A LITTLE MAD, TOO.
HERE. I GOT THESE FROM ONE OF THE SYNTHS.

AAAAHHHHH— YOU @%#*ING &%@#!S!!

THAT'S MY LIFE'S WORK— MY *LIFE'S* WORK!
I'LL KILL YOU FOR THIS!

TOUGH TALK FROM A DEAD MAN.
BRAKA BRAKA
NO!
WHAT THE HELL'S THE MATTER WITH YOU?!
I'M SORRY, SIR, BUT I CANNOT ALLOW ANY HARM TO COME TO ANY HUMAN BEING.
I AM UNABLE TO DISCRIMINATE. IT'S IN—
YEAH, YEAH, I KNOW; IT'S IN YOUR PROGRAMMING.
IN THE MEANTIME, THAT SCUMBAG IS GETTING AWAY.
GETTING AWAY TO WHERE? WE'RE INSIDE A CONTAINED ENVIRONMENT IN DEEP SPACE, AND THE TRANSPORTS ARE IN THE OTHER DIRECTION.
I ASSURE YOU, HE'S NOT GOING ANYWHERE—

"NOT ANYWHERE YOU HAVE TO WORRY ABOUT."

C'MON, LIZZY. MOVE IT, WILL YOU?
DOCTOR...

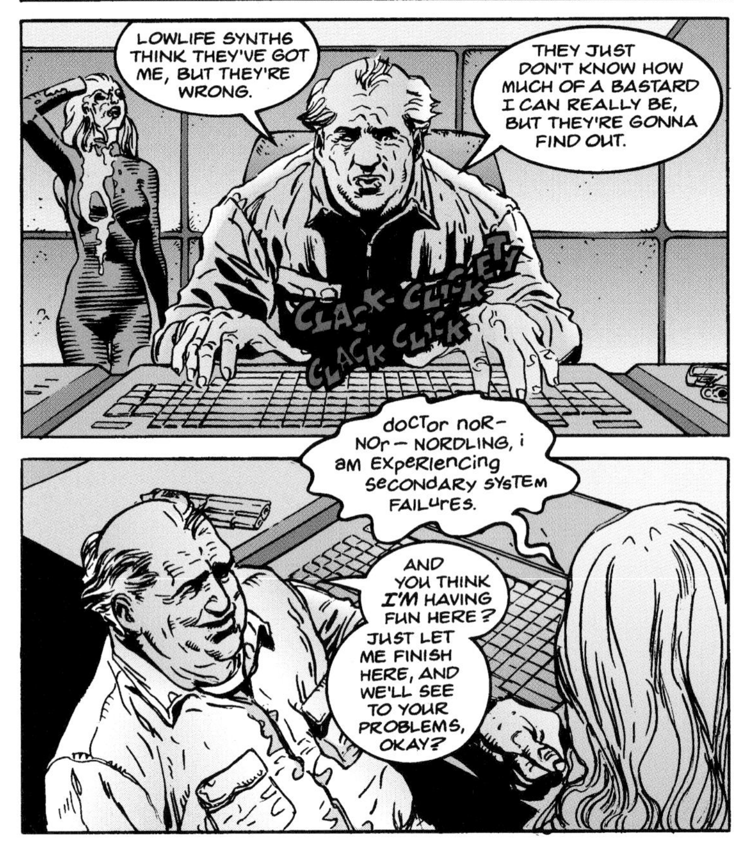
LOWLIFE SYNTHS THINK THEY'VE GOT ME, BUT THEY'RE WRONG.
THEY JUST DON'T KNOW HOW MUCH OF A BASTARD I CAN REALLY BE, BUT THEY'RE GONNA FIND OUT.
CLACK-CLICKETY
CLACK CLICK
DOCTOR NOR-NOR — NORDLING, I AM EXPERIENCING SECONDARY SYSTEM FAILURES.
AND YOU THINK I'M HAVING FUN HERE? JUST LET ME FINISH HERE, AND WE'LL SEE TO YOUR PROBLEMS, OKAY?

DOCTOR, THAT'S THE MANUAL OVERRIDE —
THAT'S RIGHT, LIZZY. THAT'S EXACTLY WHAT IT IS.

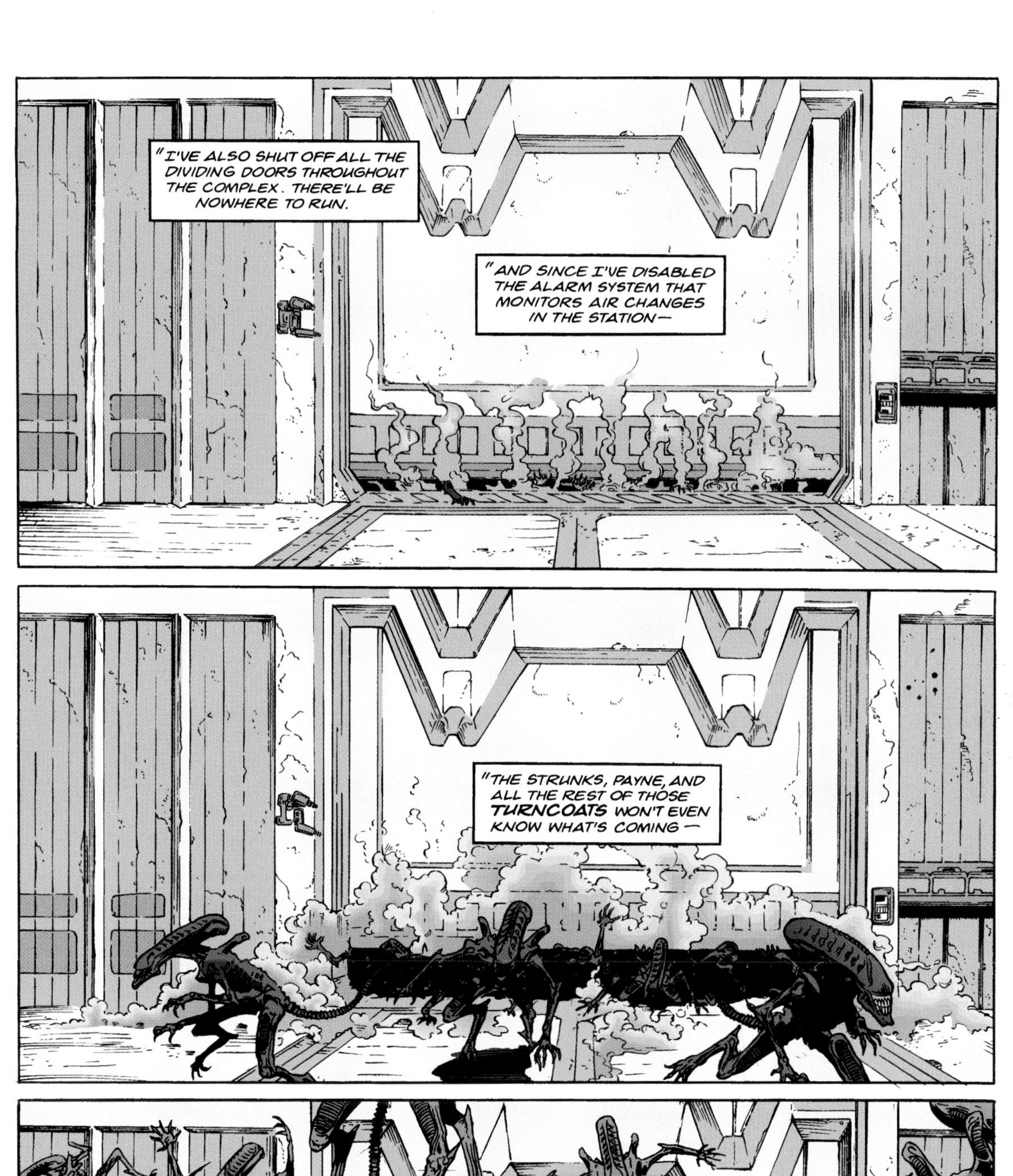
"I'VE ALSO SHUT OFF ALL THE DIVIDING DOORS THROUGHOUT THE COMPLEX. THERE'LL BE NOWHERE TO RUN.
"AND SINCE I'VE DISABLED THE ALARM SYSTEM THAT MONITORS AIR CHANGES IN THE STATION—
"THE STRUNKS, PAYNE, AND ALL THE REST OF THOSE TURNCOATS WON'T EVEN KNOW WHAT'S COMING—

"UNTIL IT'S ALREADY THERE."

OKAY NOW, DARLING. YOU TRY TO HOLD OUT JUST A LITTLE LONGER.
BUT DOCTOR, WE CAN'T GET BACK TO THE TRANSPORTS FROM HERE NOW.

WHICH IS WHY WE'RE HEADING UP TO THE TOP LEVEL— WHERE THE *EMERGENCY ESCAPE POD* IS...

"MAKING A BRIEF STOP FOR MY MONEY, OF COURSE."
I STILL THINK WE SHOULD GO AFTER NORDLING.
WE SHALL, BUT FIRST, WE MUST ALERT THE AUTHORITIES.

SINCE YOUR ONBOARD TRANSMITTER IS THE ONLY MEANS OF COMMUNICATION ON-PLANET NOT CONTROLLED BY NORDLING'S SECURITY CODE, WE'LL NEED TO GAIN ACCESS TO YOUR SHIP.
THIS WEAPON SHOULD HELP US WITH THAT.

R-R-RUUUMBLLE
WH- WHAT TH-THE F-F-F FRIG...?

OH NO!
NO USE TRYING TO FIGURE OUT HOW IT HAPPENED, JUST START SHOOTING!
UNLESS THERE'S SOMETHING "IN YOUR PROGRAMMING" ABOUT THESE THINGS, TOO!
IN FACT, THERE IS...

TOTAL EXTERMINATION!
BRAKA
BRAKA
BRAKA
BRAKA

YOU AND YOUR WIFE HAD BETTER RETREAT TO THE TRANSPORTS!
WE WILL TRY TO HOLD THE CREATURES!
THAT SOUNDS DELIGHTFUL, BUT IF YOU LOSE TWO GUNS, YOU'LL LOSE THIS FIGHT!

LISTEN UP! WE'RE ALL GOING TO FALL BACK —
— SLOWLY.

VERY... VERY... SLOWLY.

YAAA!

ANDY!

YOU'VE GOT TO BE MORE CARE-FUL.
BLAM
UHHF!
WHAT THE HELL'S GOING ON BACK THERE?!
DON'T WORRY, SIR— EVERY-THING'S UNDER CONTROL.
BLAM
UNDER CONTROL?!? LOOK AT YOU!
I CAN STILL SHOOT A GUN, SIR.

DAMN! DAMN! DAMN!
OUR DEFENSE IS FALLING APART!

WHAT ARE WE GOING TO DO ABOUT THEM?
ONLY ONE THING TO DO.

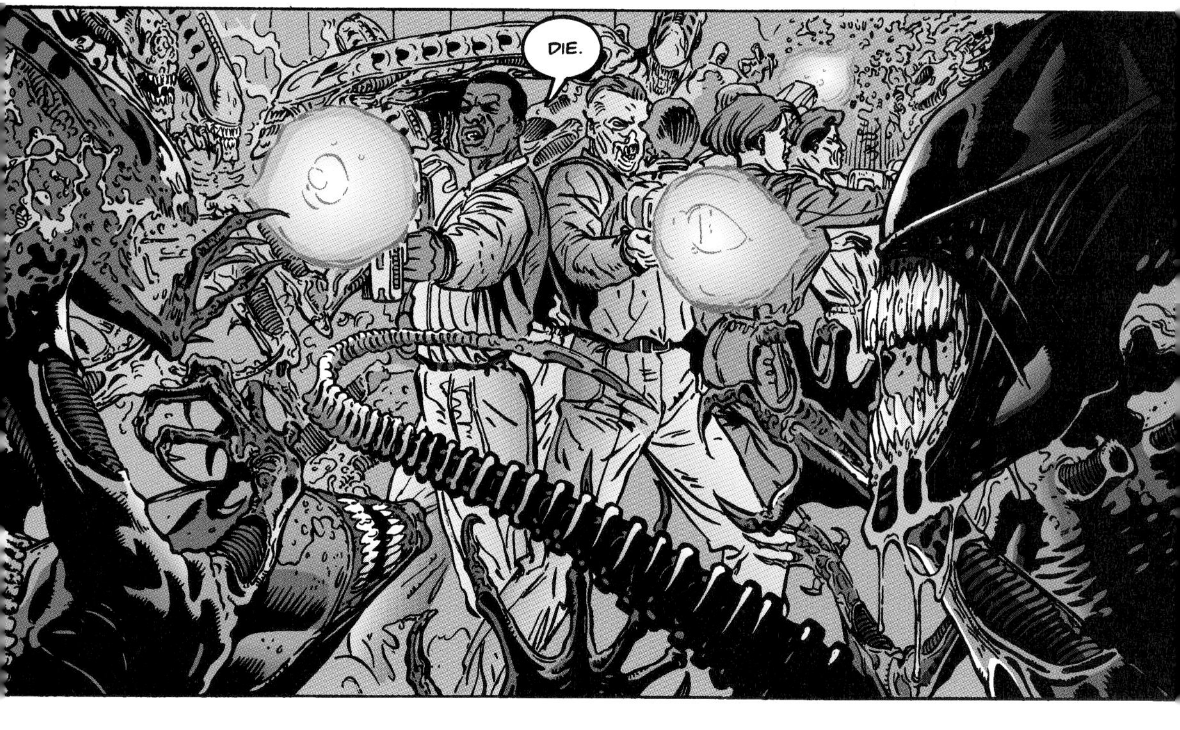
DIE.

CRR-AASH
IT'S DEAN!

MASSIVE ALIEN CREATURE PRESENCE DETECTED WITHIN HUMAN ENVIRONMENT.
YEAH, NO KIDDING! WHY AREN'T YOU FIRING?!

PERMISSION TO DISCHARGE WEAPONRY WITHIN CONFINES OF SAID ENVIRONMENT.
HUH?

AS HUMANS, YOU AND YOUR WIFE ARE THE RANKING AUTHORITY HERE.
JUST TELL HIM "PERMISSION GRANTED"!

PERMISSION GRANTED!
BOOM
BOOM
BOOM
BOOM

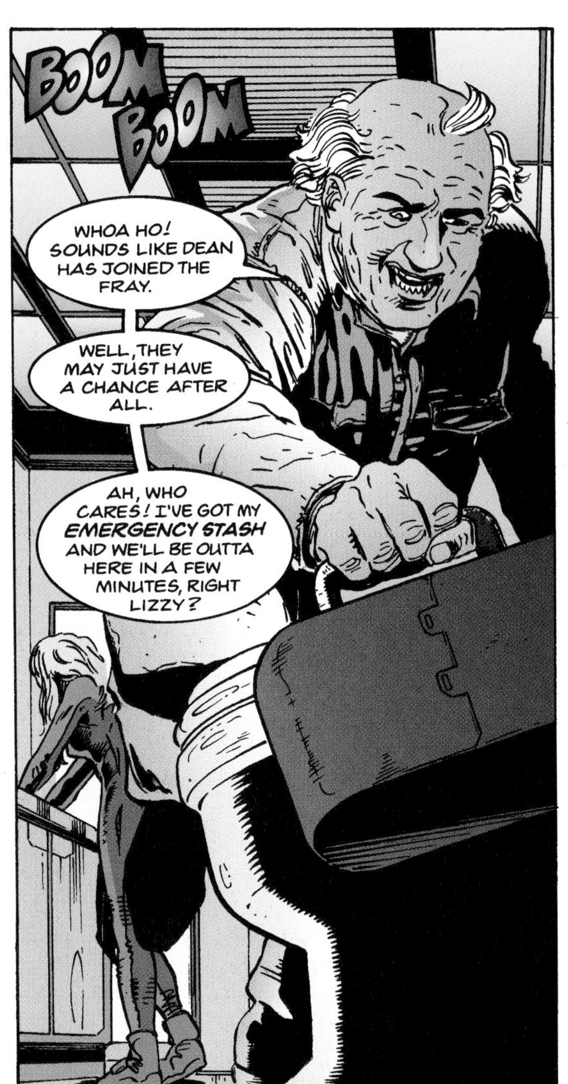
BOOM BOOM
WHOA HO! SOUNDS LIKE DEAN HAS JOINED THE FRAY.
WELL, THEY MAY JUST HAVE A CHANCE AFTER ALL.
AH, WHO CARES! I'VE GOT MY *EMERGENCY STASH* AND WE'LL BE OUTTA HERE IN A FEW MINUTES, RIGHT LIZZY?

DOCTOR, i REquiRE FLUiD iNtaKE TO continuE.

funcTIONS eRODING... geTTINg worsE —

GeTTINg worse.— geTTINg WORSE — getting WORSe —

BLAM
BLAM
BLAM
BLAM
BLAM

UHNF!

HISSSS
LIZZYYYY!

BLAM
BLAM
BLAM
BLAM

BLAM
BLAM
BLAM

doCTOR?... DOCtor?... D-d-dOCTOR...?...

HEY, THANKS A LOT, LIZZY. YOU REALLY CAME THROUGH.
tOTal... systems fail-ail-ail...
KINDA WISH I COULD HELP YOU OUT, BUT THERE'S NO WAY, OLD GIRL, NOT THE SHAPE YOU'RE IN.

DOCtOr... dOCTor... doc... doc... doc...

THE WAY TO THE TRANSPORTS IS CLEAR. DOCTOR PAYNE WILL TAKE YOU THERE.
BUT, JERI, WHAT ABOUT YOU? YOU CAN'T SURVIVE IF YOU STAY HERE.

DR. STRUNK, NONE OF US OPERATES FOR AN INFINITE TIME SPAN.

COME ON, JOY! THIS AIN'T THE TIME TO GET SENTIMENTAL!

WHAT AN ABSTRUSE WOMAN. IT'S SO DIFFICULT TO GET THINGS DONE WITH HER AROUND.

BUD-
DOOM
BLAM
BLAM

BOOM
BOOM
BOOM

GCK!

DEAN!

BOOM
BOOM

DOWN AT THE LANDING DOCK ...
BRAKA BRAKA
THAT SHOULD ABOUT DO IT. I CAN BLAST THROUGH THE OUTSIDE DOORS WITH MY SHIP'S CANNON.

YOU'RE COMING WITH US, AREN'T YOU?
I CAN'T, DOCTOR. MY PROGRAMMING WOULD ALLOW IT, BUT MY RESPONSIBILITY IS TO MY FELLOW SYNTHETICS.
IF IT'S AT ALL POSSIBLE, I'LL TRY TO REPAIR THEM.
BESIDES, IF THE CREATURES GET PAST DEAN, SOMEONE WILL HAVE TO HOLD THEM OFF.

BUT—
FOR GOD'S SAKE, JOY, GIVE IT UP!

VVRROOOM

YOU KNOW, THIS MORNING YOU ACTED AS IF YOU THOUGHT JERI WAS OUT TO KILL US AND NOW YOU'RE PRACTICALLY CRYING OVER HIM.
MY GOD, PHIL, HE SAVED OUR LIVES THREE TIMES SINCE THEN! HOW AM I SUPPOSED TO REACT?!

LOOK, I'M THANKFUL FOR THAT TOO, BUT YOU! YOU'RE PROJECTING HUMANITY ON THOSE SYNTHS, AND THEY'RE JUST MACHINES.
THEY HAVE TO ACT THAT WAY. THAT'S WHAT THEY WERE BUILT AND PROGRAMMED FOR.
JUST LIKE A COFFEE MACHINE MAKES COFFEE.

I *KNOW* THAT, BUT I CAN'T BE AS OBJECTIVE ABOUT IT AS YOU.
WHEN I SAW NORDLING ABUSE THEM, AND THEY COULDN'T FIGHT BACK, IT MADE THEM ALL SEEM SO... SO VULNERABLE.

YEAH, REAL VULNERABLE. TEAR THEM APART, AND YOU CAN PUT THEM RIGHT BACK TOGETHER AGAIN.
SPEAKING OF NORDLING, I WONDER IF HE GOT AWAY.

NO. NO WAY...

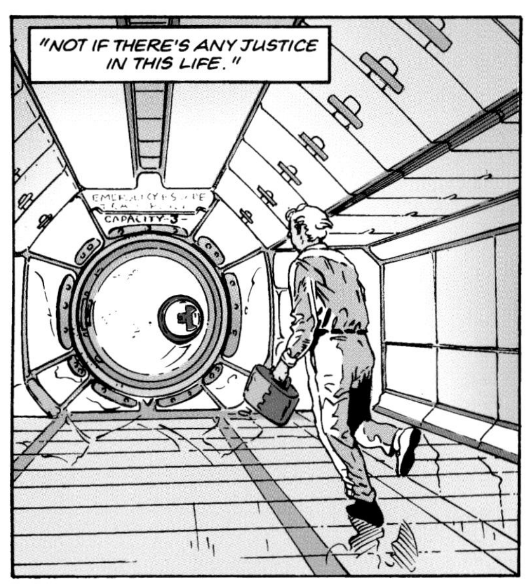
"NOT IF THERE'S ANY JUSTICE IN THIS LIFE."
CAPACITY-3-

HA HA. I MADE IT!

KVOOOOOM

HEH-HEY! ME AND MY MONEY... TOGETHER AGAIN!
GOOD THING I ALWAYS PLAN AHEAD--

YAAAAAA
HHHHHH

HHHH hello Doctor.
J-JERI?
DAMN, JERI. YOU SCARED THE CRAP RIGHT OUTTA ME.

SoRRY doCtor... DidN't Mean to, but eye — i Know WHAt will make you feel better.

...NO — KNOW WHAT will CHEer You up.

JERI ... JERI, WHERE'D YOU GET THAT CIGAR?
YOUR friEND COMMANDER CHAUT ... gAVE it TO ME ...

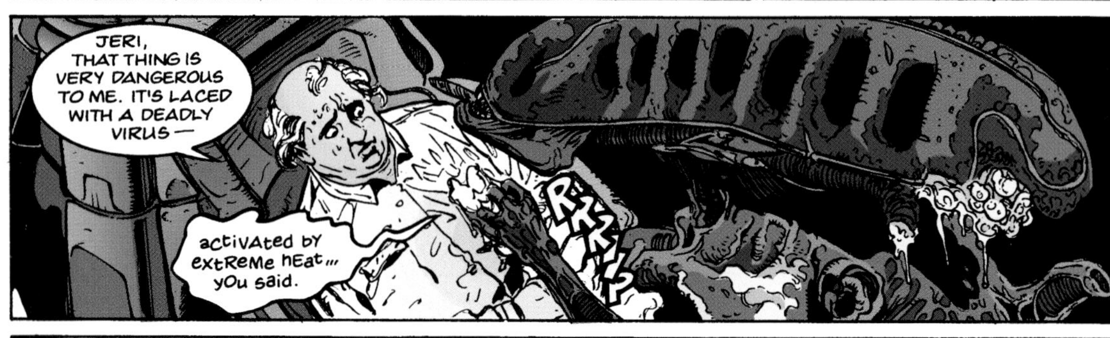
JERI, THAT THING IS VERY DANGEROUS TO ME. IT'S LACED WITH A DEADLY VIRUS —
activated by extReme heat... you said.

JERI, THAT'S MY LIGHTER!
liGHtEr... DARKER... dArkest-niGHt... Day... day-liGHT... Light... Lighter...

JERI, YOU LIGHT THAT CIGAR, YOU'LL KILL ME!
THAT'S IN DIRECT VIOLATION OF YOUR PRIME DIRECTIVE!!
damage sustained— in combat to—central processing... experiencing system --failures.
prime die-wreck-directive enforcement program has been—incapacitated.
CHIT
PUFF PUFF PUFF
but I still know a son of a bitch when I see one.

THE END

COVER GALLERY

Here, in order of appearance, are Doug Mahnke's painted covers from the ALIENS: STRONGHOLD comic-book series.